Electrical Wiring

Seventh Edition

Written and Edited by

Ralph Duncan & James E. Wren

The American Association for Vocational Instructional Materials (AAVIM) is a nonprofit association embracing universities, colleges and divisions of vocational education. Its mission is to develop, publish and distribute quality instructional materials for more effective teaching and learning. Direction for the organization is provided by representation from member states and agencies. AAVIM also collaborates with teacher organizations, government agencies and industry to provide excellence in instuctional materials.

AAVIM Staff

George W. Smith, Jr.	*Director*
James E. Wren	*Assistant Director*
Laura Ebbert	*Business Manager*
Karen Seabaugh	*Product Outsource/ Sales Manager*
Kim Lavender	*Secretary*
James A. Anderson	*Computer Graphics*
Dean Roberts	*Shipping*

Electrical Wiring Editiorial Staff

James E. Wren	*Technical Writer/ Instructional Design*
Ralph Duncan	*Technical Editor/ Consultant*
James A. Anderson	*Desktop Publishing*
Junior Trammel	*Desktop Publishing*
Carol Herring	*Typography*
James Strawser	*Photography*

For information about other AAVIM materials and services, to place and order or request a free catalog, please write or contact:

AAVIM
220 Smithonia Road
Winterville, Georgia 30683-9527
Phone: 706-742-5355
Fax: 706-742-7005
Website: www.aavim.com

ISBN: 0-89606-351-8

Printed in the United States of America

Electrical Wiring Authors

The text and illustrations for the seventh edition of *Electrical Wiring* (Copyright 1999) has been written and edited by **Ralph Duncan** and **James E. Wren**.

The text for editions one through six of *Electrical Wiring* was based on the original manuscript written and edited in 1980 by **Thomas S. Colvin**.

AAVIM is greatful to the following individuals for their assistance in the development of this publication:

Carl Scholfield
Electrical Wiring Student

Dana Perkins
Agricultural Education Instructor

Ken Hix
Electrical Inspector and Code Analyst

With deepest appreciation for the many contributions given to vocational education and to the electrical industry as teacher, administrator, author and friend, the AAVIM Board of Directors and staff greatfully dedicate this seventh edition of Electrical Wiring to Thomas S. Colvin.

Contents

Preface

The seventh edition of *Electrical Wiring*, includes information and NEC® references for basic electrical wiring principles and practices not included in earlier editions. It has been written and designed as an instructional resource text for secondary, post secondary and apprenticeship residential electrical wiring programs and addresses the basic wiring practices and skills necessary for today's electrical industry workforce. Safety is stressd throughout the publication.

The information in this publication is based on the minimum electrical standards based on the codes found in the *National Electrical Code®*. Each topic discussed and illustrated, where applicable, is referenced to the NEC® article or requirement that governs the procedure. Readers should also consult their local electrical building inspection codes before proceeding with any wiring procedure that may be in question.

Upon completing this text, you will be able to:

- Read and interpret residential wiring plans
- Identify basic wiring symbols
- Understand common electrical terms
- Identify basic tools and equipment used for residential wiring
- Understand basic electrical circuits
- Plan basic electrical residential circuits
- Identify and install common electrical device and outlet boxes.
- Identify and install common electrical cables and conductors.
- Identify and install receptacles and switches.
- Identify and install three and four-way switched circuits.
- Select and install service entrance panels and subpanels
- Install circuit breakers.
- Install grounding and bonding devices.
- Install ground fault circuit interrupters.
- Install service entrance equipment.
- Install electrical conduit.
- Install lighting fixtures.
- Estimate wiring costs and materials.

Introduction

A well-planned, properly installed residential wiring system will supply all of a home owners electrical power needs, safely and conveniently, for many years. When properly planned, it will also provide for future electrical power demands. Not only must it be well-planned and properly installed, it must also be safe. To assure that residential wiring is correctly and safely installed, most communities have adopted codes for their community.

Before you begin your study of residential electrical wiring, you should become familiar with the some of the organizations, both national and local, that set the minimum standards for safety and proper installation of electrical equipment and materials.

The need for safety standards in electrical installation was realized shortly after New York City installed the first utility system in the late 1800's. The first national electric code was established around 1911 when the **National Fire Protection Association** began its sponsorship of the **National Electric Code®**.

■ The National Electrical Code® (NFPA 70)

This code, commonly called the **NEC®** has been developed to provide uniform, minimum standards for the electrical industry. Its purpose is to provide information to assure the safe installation of electrical wiring for the protection of life and property.

The NEC®, which is revised every three years, does not carry the force of law unless adopted by the governing bodies of the state, county or local governing body where it will be applied. Local authorities may include special code requirements in addition to those found in the National Electrical Code®.

A condensed version of The National Electrical Code®, **(NFPA 70A)**, which addresses wiring procedures for one and two-family dwelling is also available. AAVIM recommends that students, instructors and electrical professionals keep current copies of both NEC® versions on hand for reference.

The NEC® is referenced throughout this text. All references to the NEC® are shown in the margins of the text (see example at right.) These code references are designed to provide a quick- reference to the proper NEC® sections and article number as they may apply to the information discussed in the text.

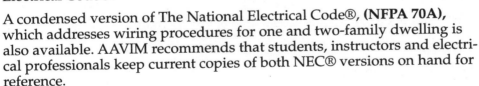

NEC® Reference For more on re-identification of conductors, see NEC® Article 200-7

Note: References to the NEC® appearing in this publication have been reprinted with permission from NFPA 70-1999, The National Electrical Code®, Copyright© 1998, National Fire Protection Association, Quincy, MA 02269. This reprinted material is not the complete and official position of the National Fire Protection Association, on the referenced subject which is represented only by the standard in its entirety.

National Electric Code® and NEC® are registered trademarks of the National Fire Protection Association, Inc., Quincy, MA 02269

◼ Local Code Amendments

Most localities require an **electrical permit** before an electrical installation can begin. It authorizes the electrician to begin the wiring installation and insures that the installation will be inspected and approved by the local **electrical inspector**. Periodic inspections are usually made at the begin ning or "rough- in" stage of construction and another upon   completion of the installation. The inspector's job is to see that the installation is in compliance with the minimum standards found in the NEC® and with local code amendments. The electrical inspection at the local level is the final authority in interpreting local codes and those found in the National Electrical Code®.

Local code amendments may exceed the standards found in the NEC® but never fall below the minimum standards defined in the Code.

◼ Underwriters Laboratories Inc. (UL)

A research and testing organization that tests electrical wiring materials to determine if electrical products meet minimum standards for safety and quality. These standards are established either by the Underwriters Laboratory or by the American National Standards Institute (ANSI). You should always look for the UL mark of approval when buying or using electrical materials and equipment. This is your assurance that electrical products meet minimum industry safety standards. Materials made by different manufacturers may all carry the UL certification mark, but some products may be more durable and provide longer service than others. Electrical products that do not carry the UL certification may be consid-ered unsafe and will likely not be approved for use by most electrical inspectors.

◼ Intertek Testing Services (ETL)

A product testing and certification organization that assures electrical products are manufactured and conform to industry standards. The ETL listed mark appears on electrical producting ranging from home comput-ers to large industrial equipment.

◼ Canadian Standards Association (CSA)

The Canadian Standards Association tests and certifies electrial products and equipment in Canada. Only products that are tested and certified by CSA (or by an organization qualified by CSA) are allowed to bear the CSA mark. CSA is an independent, not-for-profit organization supported by more than 8,000 members and has a network of offices in Canada, the U.S. and around the world.

Other organizations that offer information on safety standards and/or train-ing for the electrical industry can be found in Appendix B, page 256.

Before You Begin

In order for you to become qualified to work in the electrical profession, you must first learn and demonstrate a basic working knowledge of electricity and electrical terminology. You must demonstrate the ability to read and interpret wiring plans, diagrams and electrical symbols. You must also become familiar with basic tools and equipment and how to use them. And, most importantly, you must learn and practice safe work habits in the workplace.

In the following topics, you will learn some of this basic—and necessary—information that will start you on your way to becoming a skilled electrician.

A. Electricity and Electrical Terms

B. Wiring Plans and Symbols.

C. Safety

D. Tools and Equipment

E. Residential Framing Basics

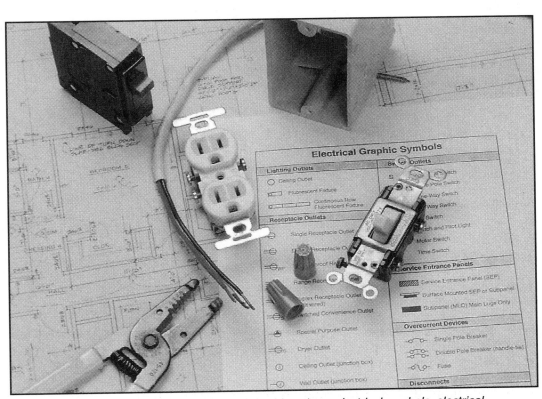

Figure 1. *A working knowledge of building and wiring plans, electrical symbols, electrical terminology, tools and equipment and safe work practices are all instrumental toward becoming a skilled, competent electrictian.*

A. Electricity & Electrical Terms

As you begin your study of how a residential wiring system works, it is important that you have a basic understanding of the product with which you will be working — **electricity.** You must also become familiar with some of the basic terminology used in the study and practice of electrical wiring. The terms shown on the opposite page are some of the most important that you will need to learn. You will see them used many times throughout this book, so learn them carefully.

Simply stated, electricity is generated by an electrical power generating plant and is transported instantaneously over a network of transmission and distribution lines, through substations and on to the consumer **(Figure 1-A-1).** Along its route from the generating plant to the consumer, electrical current is altered to avoid excessive voltage — or power — loss during the transportation process. To avoid this voltage loss, **step-up transformers** are used to increase the voltage as it leaves the power plant. Before it can be safely used by the consumer, the voltage must then be decreased by the use of **step-down transformers.**

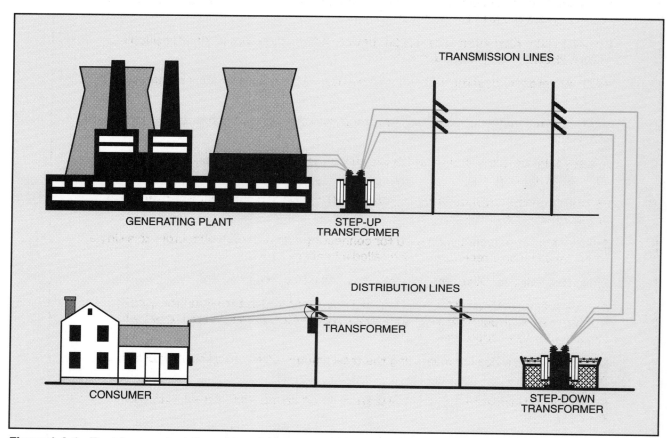

Figure 1-A-1. *Electric power is delivered from a generating faciltiy to the consumer over a network of transmission and distribution lines.*

Common Electrical Terms

Ampere (amperage) - rate at which electrical current is measured.

Cable - two or more conductors (wires) grouped together in a single unit covered by a protective sheath.

Circuit - path through which electrical current flows.

Circuit Breaker - safety device that provides overcurrent protection for a circuit.

Conductor - safety device used to control the flow of electricity in a circuit.

Current - movement of electrons through an electrical conductor.

Grounding Conductor - conductor (wire) which transmits electrical current to the earth in the event of a short circuit.

Grounded Circuit Conductor - conductor, white in color, that returns current under zero pressure from the load to the power source.

Ground Fault Circuit Interrupter (GFCI) - device that provides protection for people against shock from a short circuit.

Hot Conductor - conductor that carries electrical current to the load. An ungrounded conductor.

Load - common name for electrical equipment and devices connected to an ungrounded conductor.

Outlet - point on the circuit at which the current is utilized for receptacles, switches, appliances, lighting, etc.

Neutral Conductor - conductor that carries only the ampere imbalance between two ungrounded conductors.

Pigtail - short wire (conductor) used for connecting two or more conductors to a single screw terminal on a receptacle. Also called a jumper.

Receptacle - device allows plug in access to a circuit by plug-in.

Service Entrance Panel (SEP) - device (panel board) located in the residence which receives electrical power from the electrical supplier and is the source for branch circuits and their protection.

Service Meter - device for measuring the total amount of electrical current used in a residence.

Subpanel - panel board for additional branch circuit distribution. Receives its power from the SEP.

Switch - device that controls electrical power in the circuit.

Volt (Voltage) - measure of electrical power as it flows through a conductor.

Watt (Wattage) - measurement of the total energy consumed. Obtained by multiplying the voltage by the amperage.

Wire - common term for electrical conductor.

B. Wiring Plans & Wiring Symbols

When beginning a wiring installation in new construction, the electrician usually works from a **wiring plan**. This wiring plan is supplied by the architect or builder as part of the floor plan of the structure. The wiring plan shows the layout of the circuits, receptacles, lighting outlets and other wiring details for each room or part of the structure. An example of a typical wiring plan is shown in **Figure 1-B-1**.

Note: The wiring plan shown below will be used as an example reference throughout this publication.

Electrical symbols are used on the wiring plan to represent and indicate the type and location for ceiling outlets, switches, convenience outlets such as wall receptacles and other electrical equipment such as washers, dryers, water heaters and furnaces. Three of the most common symbols used on the wiring plan are for lighting outlets, duplex receptacles and switches. These symbols are illustrated in the wiring plan shown in **Figure 1-B-1** below. **Figure 1-B-2** shows some of the common electrical symbols with which you should become familiar if you are to successfully read and work from a wiring plan.

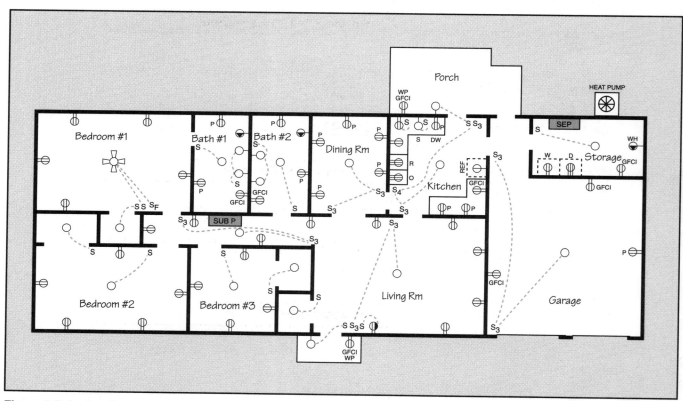

Figure 1-B-1. *A well-planned residential wiring system will supply electrial power to all parts of the home.*

Electrical Symbols

Lighting Outlets

○ Ceiling Outlet

▭ Fluorescent Fixture

▭ Continuous Row Fluorescent Fixture

Receptacle Outlets

⊖ Single Receptacle Outlet

⊖ Duplex Receptacle Outlet

⊖$_{WP}$ Weatherproof Receptacle Outlet

⊖$_R$ Range Receptacle Outlet

⊖ Duplex Receptacle Outlet (split wired)

⊖$_S$ Switched Convenience Outlet

▲ Special Purpose Outlet

⊖$_D$ Dryer Outlet

Ⓙ Ceiling Outlet (junction box)

Ⓙ Wall Outlet (junction box)

⊖$_{GFCI}$ Ground Fault Circuit Interrupter

⊖$_P$ GFCI Protected Receptacle

Ⓡ Recessed Fixture Outlet

Switch Outlets

S Single Pole Switch

S$_2$ Double Pole Switch

S$_3$ Three-Way Switch

S$_4$ Four-Way Switch

S$_F$ Fan Switch

S$_P$ Switch and Pilot Light

Ⓜ Motor Switch

Ⓣ Time Switch

Service Entrance Panels

▨ Service Entrance Panel (SEP)

▬ Surface Mounted SEP or Subpanel

▬ Subpanel (MLO) Main Lugs Only

Overcurrent Devices

⊸o⊶ Single Pole Breaker

⊸o⊶ Double Pole Breaker (handle-tie)

⊸ᘐ⊶ Fuse

Disconnects

Non-Fusable

Fusable

Figure 1-B-2. *Common electric symbols.*

C. Electrical Safety

An important consideration when working with electricity, whether on a construction site or around the home, is **SAFETY.** You should begin to develop and practice safe working habits as part of the skills you'll need to become a safe, competent electrician. Listed below are a few common sense safety rules you should learn and follow at all times. By following these simple rules, you will help protect yourself — and your fellow workers from accidents that commonly occur at the work site **(Figure 1-C-1).**

- **Wear Protective Head Gear -** Wearing a protective hard hat will help protect you from falling objects and other types of head injuries.

- **Wear Appropriate Clothing -** Work clothing should fit well and be free of flapping pockets that might get caught on projections or power tools. They should also be made of materials of low flammability. Synthetic materials with a low flash point should be avoided.

- **Wear Safety Boots Or Shoes -** Protective foot wear equipped with steel toes and rubber heels and soles will help protect against painful foot injuries and insulate against dangerous electrical shock.

- **Wear Safety Glasses/ Goggles -** Safety glasses or goggle will help protect your eyes when working around flying particles or caustic fluids that may cause eye damage.

- **Wear Gloves -** Gloves are a good method of protecting the hands and wrists from cuts, scrapes and burns.

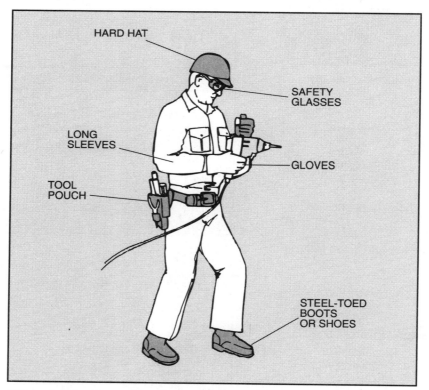

Figure 1-C-1. *Always wear protective clothing and use safety insulated tools when working with electricity.*

- **Use Insulated Power Tools -** Use only UL listed, double insulated power tools. They offer added protection against electric shock **(Figure 1-C-2)**.

- **Use Insulated Hand Tools -** Hand tools such as screwdrivers and pliers should have insulated handles for protection against shock **(Figure 1-C-3)**.

- **Protect Power Tool Cords -** Protect power tools and their cords by correctly removing the plug from the receptacle. Grasp and pull directly on the plug. Never pull or jerk on the power cord. In traffic areas, protect power cords and extension cords with boards or planks **(Figure 1-C-4)**.

- **Use Ground Fault Circuit Interrupters -** When using power tools during construction, use Ground Fault Circuit Interrupters **(GFCI)** to help protect against electrical shock. Portable GFCI's like the one shown in **Figure 1-C-5** can easily be moved from one site to another. If the power source at the worksite is not protected by a permanent type GFCI, the portable type is required.

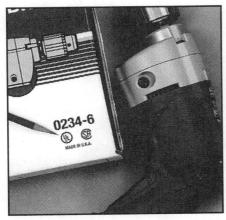

Figure 1-C-2. *Make sure power tools are UL listed.*

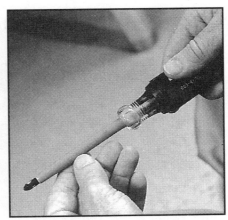

Figure 1-C-3. *Use insulated hand tools.*

Figure 1-C-4. *In high traffic areas on the work site, protect power cords with boards.*

Figure 1-C-5. *Use GFCI protection on the work site.*

- **Use Ladders Safely** - Use only wooden or fiberglass ladders for electrical work. Check the condition of your ladders regularly. Repair loose or broken rungs immediately. Make sure all braces are locked securely in place **(Figure 1-C-6)**. Have someone hold the ladder at its base if you are unsure of its stability. Never leave tools or other objects on ladder steps. And always read the safety information on the ladder before use.

- **Use Caution When Working In Wet Or Damp Areas -** When using power tools in wet or damp areas, always stand on a rubber mat or other non-conducting material for protection against shock **(Figure 1-C-7)**.

- **NEVER Work On A "Hot" Electrical Circuit -** Always disconnect the power at the service entrance panel or subpanel before you begin work on a circuit by turning the circuit breaker to the "off" position. Post a warning on the cover of the panel box to prevent someone from resetting the breaker while you are working. Additionally, you can test the circuit on which you will be working by using a circuit tester **(Figure 1-C-8)** or by plugging a lamp into the circuit to see if it is receiving current.

- **Keep A Clean Work Area** - Develop good housekeeping habits around the worksite. A cleaner work area is a safer work area **(Figure 1-C-9)**.

Author's Note:
Never assume that a circuit in not energized; always test the circuit more than once before assuming it has been de-energized.

Figure 1-C-6. Use only safety approved' fiber glass or wooden ladders.

Figure 1-C-7. Use rubber mats or other non-conducting materials when using power tools in wet areas.

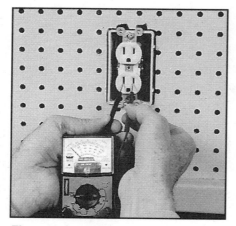

Figure 1-C-8. Always test the circuit to see if it is energized.

Figure 1-C-9. Keep your work area clean and free from debris.

D. Tools & Equipment

When performing wiring tasks, you must become skilled in selecting and using basic tools to accomplish the job. Some may be common hand and power tools with which you are already familiar while others may be special tools designed specifically for special wiring needs. Tools should always be kept good working condition; cutting tools should be kept sharp; damaged tools should be repaired or replaced. Always make sure that power tool cords and plugs are in good condition.

Tools and equipment necessary to complete a wiring installation are:

▪ **Screwdrivers (Figure 1-D-1) -** Screwdrivers come in various types and sizes. Common types are: **(a) flat blade, (b) phillips and (c) robertson.**

▪ **Pliers (Figure 1-D-2) -** Pliers of various types probably rank first among tools most frequently used by electricians .

- **(a) Round nose pliers -** Used for a variety of tasks.

- **(b) Long nose pliers -** Also called needle nose pliers. Useful for bending loops in conductors when making connections for switches and receptacles.

- **(c) Locking pliers -** Used for gripping, holding and pulling electrical cable.

- **(d) Lineman's pliers -** Available in several sizes. Most popular sizes are 7 and 8-inch models. The flat jaws will bend, grip, pull and twist light or heavy conductors and cables. The side cutting jaws will cut large cable sizes and the shoulders will crush cable insulation to make the cutting task easier.

- **(e) Water pump pliers -** Also known as channel locking pliers. Used to tighten locknuts and cable connectors.

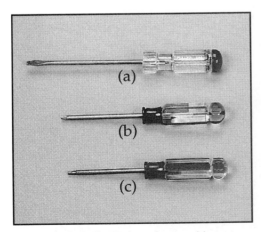

Figure 1-D-1. Examples of screwdrivers.

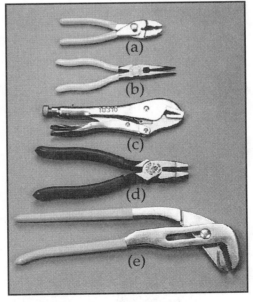

Figure 1-D-2. Examples of pliers.

■ **Wire Cutters /Cable Strippers - (Figure 1-D-3)** - Used to cut and remove insulation from conductors without damaging wire. **(a) Cable strippers. (b & c) Electricians tools.**

■ **Wrenches (Figure 1-D-4)** - Two common type are:

- **(a) Adjustable jaw wrench -** Comes in several sizes. Common sizes are 8 and 10 -inch models. Also called a Crescent wrench.

- **(b) Pipe wrench -** Used for gripping and turning round pipe and conduit.

■ **Drills (Figure 1-D-5)**

- **(a) Cordless Electric Drill -** Popular because of its convenience. Requires no power source.

- **(b) AC Power Drill -** Popular tool used for drilling holes in framing members. Requires power source.

- **(c) Push Drill -** Manual hand drill used for drilling small holes.

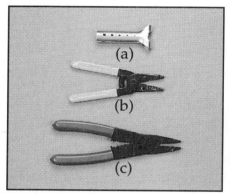

Figure 1-D-3. *Examples of wire cutters and cable strippers.*

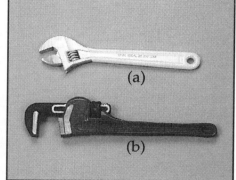

Figure 1-D-4. *Examples of wrenches.*

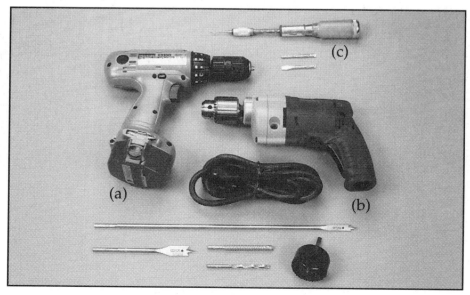

Figure 1-D-5. *Examples of drilling tools.*

■ **Measuring Tools (Figure 1-D-6)**

- **(a) Folding rule** - Made of wood or plastic. Commonly available in lengths of 6, 8 and 10-feet.

- **(b) Retractable tape** - Common measuring tool of electricians. Comes in various lengths from 6 to 100 - feet long.

■ **Plumb Bob (Figure 1-D-7)** - Weight with string attached. Used to find true perpendicular line .

■ **Level (Figure 1-D-8)** - Useful for horizontal and vertical leveling jobs.

(a) Carpenters level. (b) Torpedo level.

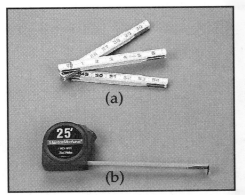

Figure 1-D-6. *Examples of measuring tools.*

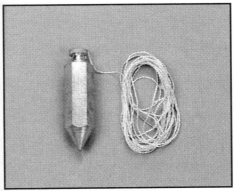

Figure 1-D-7. *A plumb bob.*

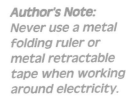

Author's Note:
Never use a metal folding ruler or metal retractable tape when working around electricity.

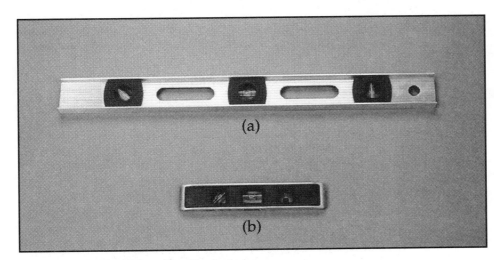

Figure 1-D-8. *Examples of leveling tools.*

■ **Cutting Tools (Figure 1-D-9)**

- **(a) Pocket knife** - Also used to strip cable sheath and taper insulation on conductors.

- **(b) Diagonal cutters** - Exposed, tapered jaws are convenient for cutting cable in utility boxes and where close fitting connections may be necessary.

- **(c) Wood Chisels** - Used for cutting and gouging wood.

- **(d) Crosscut saw** - Used for general wood sawing.

- **(e) Compass saw** - Also called keyhole saw. Used for cutting holes in flooring, wallboard and paneling.

- **(f) Hacksaw** - Used for small metal cutting jobs including large cables, conductors and conduit.

- **(g) Electric saber saw** - Versatile tool for cutting wood, metal, fiberboard and wallboard.

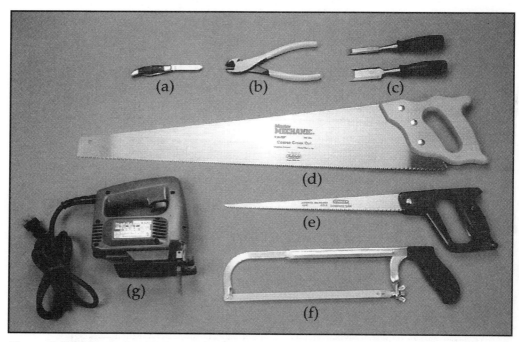

Figure 1-D-9. *Examples of cutting tools.*

- **Hammers (Figure 1-D-10)** -Used for nailing device boxes in place and other assorted uses.

- **Fish Tape (Figure 1-D-11)** - Used to pull or push cable through conduit or wall cavities.

- **Conduit Bender (Figure 1-D-12)** - Special tool used for bending metal electrical conduit.

- **Volt-Ohm Meter (Figure 1-D-13)** - A device used to test circuits for voltage and continuity.

- **Tool Belt (Figure 1-D-14)** - Used for carrying hand tools. May be constructed of leather or heavy fabric.

Figure 1-D-10. Types of hammers.

Figure 1-D-11. A fish tape.

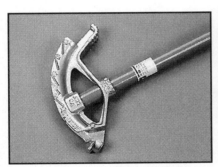

Figure 1-D-12. A conduit bender.

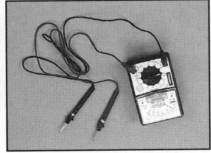

Figure 1-D-13. A volt-Ohm meter.

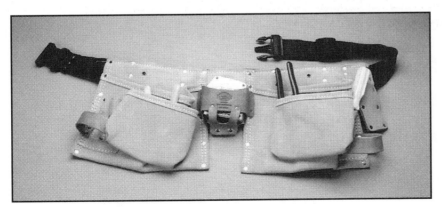

Figure 1-D-14. A workman's tool belt.

E. Residential Framing Basics

You must also become familiar with the structural famework of the house where the electrical system will be installed. Most residential construction methods of today consist of the time honored wood frame construction **(Figure 1-E-1)**. This type of construction has been, and continues to be, the predominate construction method. However, metal frame construction, once used primarily for commercial construction, has steadily grown in popularity for residential construction **(Figure 1-E-2)**.

Both framing types and how each relates to a particular electrical installation application are discussed in this publication. Whether the construction method is wood or metal, the structural parts of each are known by the same name. Knowing the names of these structural parts will help you better understand where and how the electrical system will be installed.

House plans contain many terms that refer to the different structural parts of the house. However, there are parts of the framing structure you should be able to easily identify as you develop your basic skills and knowledge .

Figure 1-E-1. *Example of typical wood frame construction.*

Figure 1-E-2. *Example of metal frame construction*

Figure 1-E-3 illustrates the major structural parts of a typical wood or metal frame dwelling:

- **Footing -** The below grade concrete base on which the foundation is constructed.

- **Foundation -** The base of the structure on which the rest of the framework of the house will is constructed.

- **Sill Plate -** Wood structure which rests on the top of the foundation and forms frame to which the floors joists are attached.

- **Floor Joists -** Horizontal framing members that attach to the sill plate and form the structural support for the floor and walls. Usually made 2"x8", 2"X 10" or 2"X12" lumber.

- **Subfloor -** The first layer of flooring material and covers the floor joists. Usually made of 4"x8" plywood sheets or particle board. Can also be made from 1"X 6" lumber.

- **Bottom Plate -** The lower or horizontal structural part of the wall frame. Rests on top of the subfloor. Usually made of 2'x4" or 2'x6' lumber

- **Wall Studs -** Used in forming the vertical portion of the wall framework. Usually 2"x4" or 2"x6" lumber.

- **Top Plate -** The top horizontal portion of the wall framework. Also made of 2'x4" or 2"x6" lumber.

- **Ceiling Joists -** Horizontal framing members that rest on top of the wall framing and forms the ceiling framework.

- **Rafters -** Framework supported by the top plate and forms the roof structure of the building.

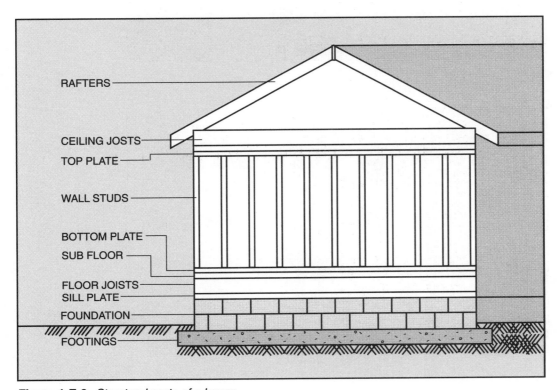

Figure 1-E-3. Structural parts of a house.

Notes

Electrical Circuits

2

An electrical **circuit** can be defined as two or more **conductors** (wires) through which electric **current** flows from a **power source** through an electrical **cable** to one or more **outlets**. The electrical cable is comprised of the two or more conductors which are usually made of copper or aluminum wire.

To help you better understand how circuits work and how they relate to the residential wiring system, see **Figure 2-1** below. The power supplier, usually the local utility company, supplies electric power from a generating plant to the residence. On its way to the consumer, it travels through the **service drop, service entrance head**, **service meter** and the **service entrance panel** where branch circuits distribute it throughout the residence. Different types of circuits originate in the SEP and distribute electrical power to all parts of the residence for lighting, receptacle outlets, small appliances, large appliances and a variety of other uses necessary in today's modern homes.

In this chapter, you will learn:

A. Principles of an Electrical Circuit

B. Parts of an Electrical Circuit

C. Types of Electrical Circuits

D. Types of Branch Circuits

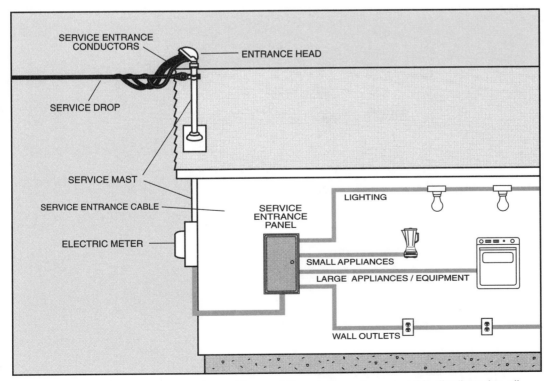

Figure 2-1. *Electrial power enters the residence at the service entrance and is distributed to all parts of the residence through a network of electrial circuits.*

A. Principles of an Electrical Circuit

Electrical circuits in a residential wiring system can be compared to a residential plumbing system. In the plumbing system, water enters a residence in a water pipe under a specific pressure. After it has been used, it then exits the residence in a drain pipe at zero pressure. Likewise, electricity enters a residence under pressure through an **ungrounded circuit conductor**. It is commonly called the **hot** conductor. The pressure at which electricity is transmitted is called its **voltage**. After it serves its intended uses such as providing lighting, running kitchen appliances or providing power for the heating /cooling system, etc., it is returned to its power source at zero pressure through a **grounded circuit conductor**.

Just as the size of a water pipe determines how much water it is capable of carrying, the size of an electrical conductor determines how much electrical current it is capable of carrying. The current carrying capacity of a conductor is called its **amperage**—also called ampacity.

Black conductors are usually considered as **ungrounded circuit conductors** and carry voltage from the power source to the load. **White** conductors are usually considered as **grounded circuit conductors** and return current from the load after use to the power source under no (zero) voltage. However, as you will learn, there can be exceptions to this general rule.

Figure 2-A-1 below illustrates a simple lighting circuit. The current is carried in the **black, ungrounded circuit conductor** under pressure (voltage) from the power source, to the lighting outlet. It then exits the lighting outlet and is returned at zero pressure (no voltage) to the power source in the **white, grounded circuit conductor**.

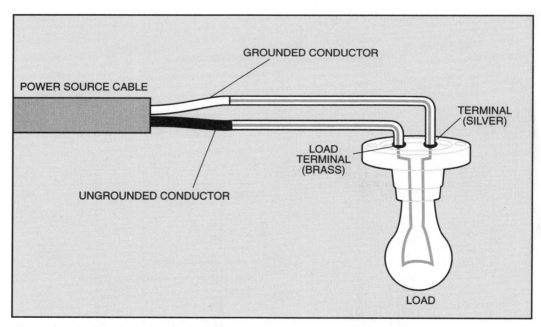

Figure 2-A-1. *Principle of a simple lighting circuit.*

#12 AWG ~~AGW~~ is used for 20 amp service

B. Parts of an Electrical Circuit

A typical residential circuit is comprised of the following basic parts. Each performs a special function in the circuit to make sure the circuit will work properly and safely. How each part works and how it is installed will be discussed in the following chapters.

- **Service Entrance** - The **service entrance (Figure 2-B-1)**, also called the **weather head**, is the point of entry for electrical service from the utility supplier to the residence.

- **Electric Meter** - The **electric meter (Figure 2-B-2)** is an instrument designed for measuring the amount of electrial power consumed by the customer.

- **Service Entrance Panel** - The **service entrance panel (Figure 2-B-3)**, commonly called the SEP, is the termination point in the circuit where the power from the utility company is connected to the residential electrical wiring system. It is also the termination point for all branch circuits in the wiring system.

- **Subpanel** - The **subpanel** provides additional branch circuits space to the system and reduces the need for long circuit runs **(Figure 2-B-4)**.

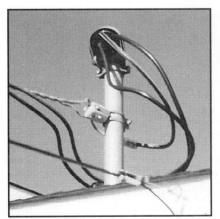

Figure 2-B-1. *A service entrance head.*

Figure 2-B-2. *An electric meter.*

Figure 2-B-3. *A service entrance panel.*

Figure 2-B-4. *A subpanel.*

- **Circuit Breakers** - **Circuit breakers** are technically **overcurrent protection devices** designed to protect the circuit from overload. **Single-pole** circuit breakers **(Figure 2-B-5)** protect 120-volt circuits and **double-pole** circuit breakers **(Figure 2-B-6)** protect 240-volt circuits.

- **Switches** - **Switches** are devices that control electrical current that passes through them **(Figure 2-B-7)**. They are commonly used for controlling lighting and small and large residential appliances and equipment.

- **Receptacles** - **Receptacles** provide easy plug-in access to the electrical power provided by the electrical system **(Figure 2-B-8)**. They are also commonly referred to as **convenience outlets** or **wall outlets.**

- **Electrical Cables/ Conductors** - Electrical conductors Figure 2-B-9), commonly called "**wire,**" create the path that carries electrical current through the circuit. Conductors are available in a variety of sizes and types, each rated for the requirements of the circuit.

Figure 2-B-5. *A single-pole circuit breaker.*

Figure 2-B-6. *A double-pole circuit breaker.*

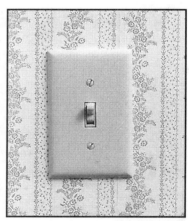

Figure 2-B-7. *A wall switch.*

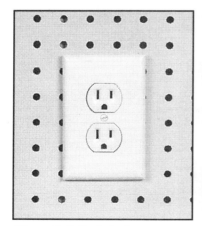

Figure 2-B-8. *A duplex receptacle.*

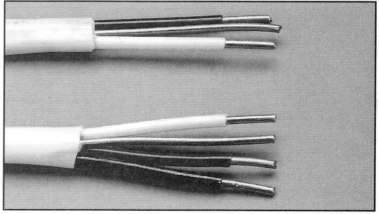

Figure 2-B-9. *Electrical conductors must be rated for the requirements of the circuit.*

C. Types of Electrical Circuits

There are two basic types of electrical circuits used in a residential wiring system:

(1) Branch Circuits

(2) Feeder Circuits

◼ Branch Circuits

Branch circuits are defined as the conductors between the circuit breaker and the last outlet, switch or receptacle on the circuit. Most circuits installed in residences are of the branch circuits type. They run from the circuit breaker in the SEP, or the subpanel, to one or more outlets, such as lights or receptacles **(Figure 2-C-1).** Each branch circuit is protected by its own circuit breaker.

NEC® References For more on branch circuits, see NEC® Articles 210 220

Having several branch circuits in a home wiring system make the home wiring system more efficient and less expensive to install. When several circuits are installed, each circuit can be assigned a specific use. This arrangement offers more convenience to the homeowner and it is less expensive to install since smaller, less costly electrical cables are used for the smaller circuits. Larger circuits, those that serve large appliances and equipment, require larger and more expensive electrical cable.

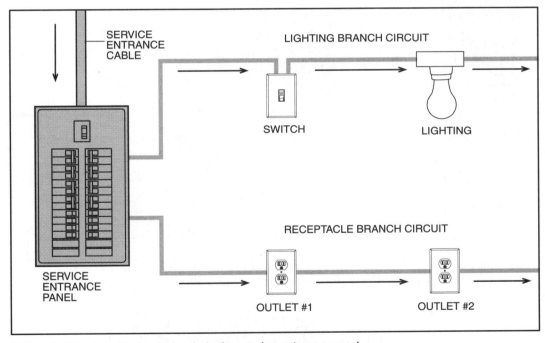

Figure 2-C-1. *Branch circuits begin in the service entrance panel and supply power to all parts of a residence.*

■ Feeder Circuits

Feeder circuits are defined as those circuits that run between the SEP and a subpanel **(Figure 2-C-2)**. A feeder circuit may also originate at a generator or battery. In larger homes, subpanels are often necessary when additional breaker positions are needed. Subpanels also help guard against potential voltage drops caused by excessively long branch circuit runs.

In new construction, the NEC® has required a method for disconnecting electrical service from a location outside the residence. This type of installation requires a service panel with outside disconnect to be located outside the residence and a subpanel, connected by a feeder cable, which is usually located inside the residence. The subpanel may or may not be equipped with a main breaker disconnect on the panel board. It is not required

Local electrical codes are rapidly recognizing this minimum NEC® requirement and are enforcing the use of an SEP with an outside disconnect in combination with an inside subpanel as part of their electrical requirements.

NEC® References
For more on
feeder circuits, see
NEC® Articles
100
215
220
230-70a

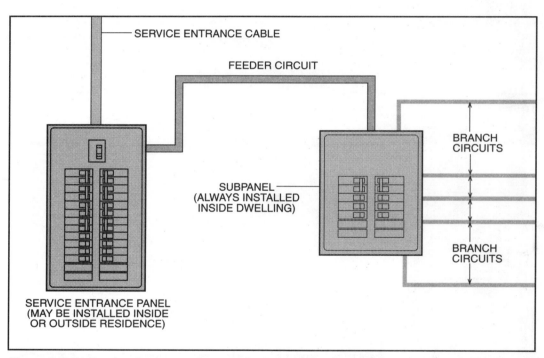

Figure 2-C-2. *Feeder circuits supply power from the service entrance panel to the subpanel.*

D. Types of Branch Circuits

There are three common types of branch circuit. Each is designated to handle the specific and different requirements of the residential wiring system. They are:

(1) General Purpose Branch Circuits

(2) Small Appliance Branch Circuits

(3) Individual Equipment Branch Circuits (DEDICATED) circuit

Each of the three types is discussed in this section along with the special require ments for bathroom circuits.

■ General Purpose Branch Circuits

General purpose branch circuits make up a major portion of the residential wiring system. They include all lighting outlets and most convenience receptacles and are typically installed using **No. 14 AWG** and **No. 12 AWG** wiring cable and require **15-ampere** and **20-ampere** overcurrent protection devices (circuit breakers).

The NEC® refers to these types of circuits as "lighting "circuits, but to call them general purpose circuits better describes their function **(Figures 2-D-1)**. While they supply power to the lighting system of the residence, they also provide the electrical power for items like radios, vacuum cleaners, televisions, computers and many other uses in the typical residence.

NEC® References
For more on branch circuits, see
NEC® Articles
200
210-24
210-52a

Author's Note:
Check your local code before installing #14 AWG conductors for residential branch circuit use; It sometimes results in excessive low voltage drop resulting in poor equipment performance.

Figure 2-D-1. *General purpose circuits supply power for most lighting and general household use.*

■ Small Appliance Branch Circuits

Small appliance branch circuits are those that generally supply power to kitchen counter top surfaces and dining room areas where small appliances are commonly used. Some typical household appliances that use small appliance circuits are coffee makers, **(Figure 2-D-2)** fry pans, blenders, toaster ovens and waffle irons.

NEC® References
For more on small
appliance branch
circuits, see
NEC® Article
210-8
210-52b

The NEC® requires that small appliance circuits be installed using a minimum **No. 12-2 AWG with ground** electrical cable protected at the SEP or subpanel with a **20-ampere** circuit breaker. The NEC® also demands that in specific instances, certain safety installation regulations be followed. Some of these are:

- Countertop kitchen receptacles must be served by a <u>**minimum**</u> of two **(2)** small appliance circuits. These circuits may be extended to serve <u>only</u> the receptacle outlets in other adjacent rooms such as the pantry, breakfast room, and dining room. If more than two small appliance circuits are installed, the additional circuit may also serve receptacle outlets in these same areas.

Author's Note:
All kitchen
countertop
receptcles
must be GFCI
protected.

- Outlets, other than those specified by the NEC®, **<u>are not permitted</u>** on small appliance circuits. However, the NEC® permits the following exceptions to this regulation.

  1. A small appliance circuit may be used to supply power to a clock outlet.

  2. Small appliance circuits may supply power for electric ignitions and timers for gas ranges.

  3. Certain motor loads such as refrigerators may be supplied power by small appliance circuits **(Figure 2-D-3)**.

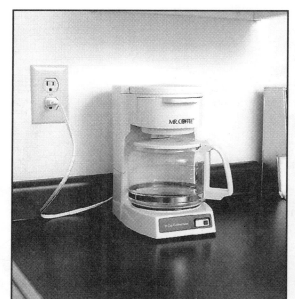

Figure 2-D-2. *A coffee maker is typical of the types of appliances served by small appliance circuits.*

Figure 2-D-3. *Refrigerators may be installed on small appliance circuits.*

◼ Individual Equipment Branch Circuits

Individual equipment circuits are classified as those that supply current to only one appliance or piece of equipment. They are also called **dedicated circuits.** They serve large appliances or other equipment that require larger amounts of electrical current to operate than do small appliance or general purpose circuits.

Individual equipment circuits typically require 240-volts or a combination of 120/240-volts. These circuits also require larger cable sizes and larger overcurrent protection devices. However, some individual circuits such as garbage disposal units, dishwashers, trash compacters room air conditioners, and refrigerators require only 120-volt circuits installed with No. 12 AWG conductors and 20-ampere circuit breakers. A heat pump is an example of a of large electrical unit that requires an individual circuit **(Figure 2-D-4)**.

NEC® References
For more on
individual
branch circuits,
see NEC® Article
422

Some other common examples of appliances and equipment served by individual branch circuits include ranges, clothes dryers, heating and cooling systems, water heaters, dishwashers, garbage disposals, trash compactors, permanent bathroom heaters, large microwave ovens and food freezers.

◼ Bathroom Branch Circuits

The NEC® requires that bathrooms be served by a special 20-ampere circuit to serve **only** bathrooms. No other outlets are allowed to be connected to these circuits. All receptacles on these circuits must also be GFCI protected **(Figure 2 D-5)**.

NEC® Reference
for more on
bathroom
branch circuits, see
NEC® Articles
210-8a[1]
210-52d

The NEC® regulation permits a single, 20-ampere circuit to serve two bathrooms. However, with the the ever increasing electrical loads required in most modern bathrooms and adjoining dressing areas, good judgment calls for separate 20 ampere circuits for each bathroom.

Figure 2-D-4. Heating and cooling equipment is installed on individual circuits.

Figure 2-D-5. All bathroom circuits must must be GFCI protected and serve only bathrooms.

In summarizing what you've learned thus far, take a look at **Figure 2-D-6** below. It illustrates the key components that make up a typical residental wiring system. The power arrives at the residence at the entrance head, passes through the meter and into the service entrance panel. From the service entrance panel, the power is distributed to all parts of the house by general purpose, small appliance and individal branch circuits. Should the wiring plan call for a subpanel, a feeder circuit is installed to a breaker in the service entrance panel to provide the power. Additional branch circuits can then be installed in the subpanel. A well designed wiring system can deliver all the requirements necessary for today's modern lifestyles.

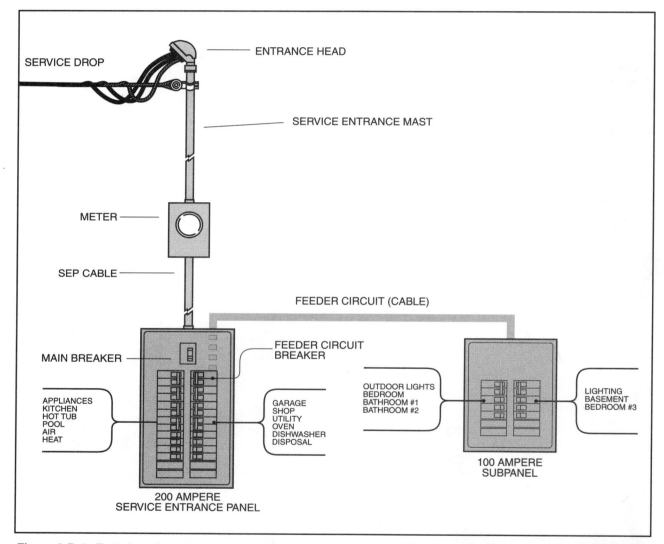

Figure 2-D-6. *Today's residential wiring systems are designed to meet all the requirements of family living and leisure.*

Planning Circuits

3

Now that you've been introduced to some of the basic terminology and principles necessary for electrical wiring practices, you can begin the important process of planning the different types of circuits that are required in a typical residential wiring system **(Figure 3-1)**.

You've already been introduced to circuits, wiring plans and electrical symbols and the important roll they play in the wiring system. In this chapter, you will learn the basic steps for planning electrical circuits including the following topics.

A. Planning Service Entrance Panels and Subpanel Locations.

B. Outlet Spacing Requirements

C. Marking Outlet Locations for Circuit Runs.

D. Planning Small Appliance Branch Circuits.

E. Planning General Purpose Branch Circuits.

F. Planning Individual Branch Circuits.

G. Planning Bathroom Branch Circuits.

Figure 3-1. *Planning the electrial wiring system is one of the most important steps in the electrial installation process.*

The wiring plan shown in **Figure 3-2**, page 29, shows the general placement of wall and ceiling outlets, switches, locations for major appliances, special equipment and the SEP and subpanel. Wiring plans supplied by architectural and electrical engineering firms often indicate the circuit routes by a system of lines that connect the outlets and switches in the wiring system. However, wiring plans used for most residential wiring systems do not indicate which outlets will be combined to make up a circuit. This responsibility falls on the electrician to decide how best to combine outlets into a circuit.

As you plan the circuits on the wiring plan, the lines you will use to connect outlets in the circuit represent the electrical cable that makes the connection between outlets in the wiring system **(Figure 3-3)**.

- **Solid lines** represent a **cable run** (circuit) starting in the service entrance panel and connecting with each outlet on the circuit. It is also sometimes referred to as a **"home run."** Solid lines may also represent a circuit cable that is connected from the SEP directly to an appliance or other piece of equipment that might require an individual circuit.

- **Dotted lines** represent a cable connection between a switch and to a lighting outlet or other special receptacle outlets controlled by a switch. They are also called **switch legs** or **switch loops**.

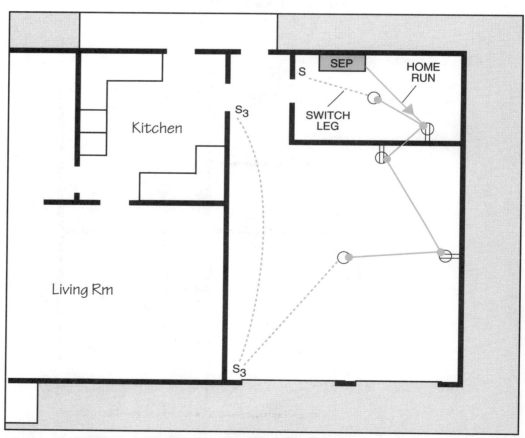

Figure 3-3. On the wiring plan, solid lines represent an electrial circuit. Dotted lines on the wiring plan represent switches on the circuit.

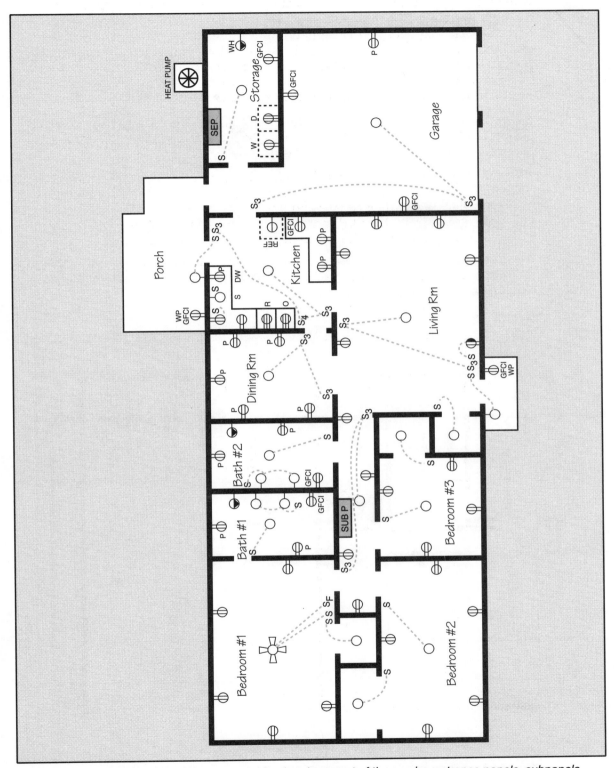

Figure 3-2. *The wiring plan is the guide used for the placement of the service entrance panels, subpanels, receptacle outlets, switches, appliances and other large electrial equipment.*

A. Planning Service Entrance Panels and Subpanel Locations

You should begin planning your circuit runs by first locating the **service entrance panel and/or subpanel** on the wiring plan.

NEC® References
For more on service
entrance panels and
subpanels, see
NEC® Articles
384-4
384-8

The service entrance panel **(SEP)** should always be located as near as possible to the service entrance **(Figure 3-A-1).** Check the wiring plan with your power supplier to determine where the electric service will enter the residence. It is also desirable to locate the SEP near the appliances and equipment that will require the most power. This will reduce the length of the larger conductors required by appliances such as the electric water heaters, clothes dryers and furnaces. It also reduces the cost of labor and materials. The subpanel, like the SEP should be located central to the areas of the house that its circuits will serve.

The SEP and the subpanel should be located in areas of the residence that are accessible at all times. When selecting a site for locating the panel boards, consider not only its present use, but also power needs that may be anticipated in the future. The NEC® prohibits locating the SEP or the subpanel in a clothes closet or in bathrooms.

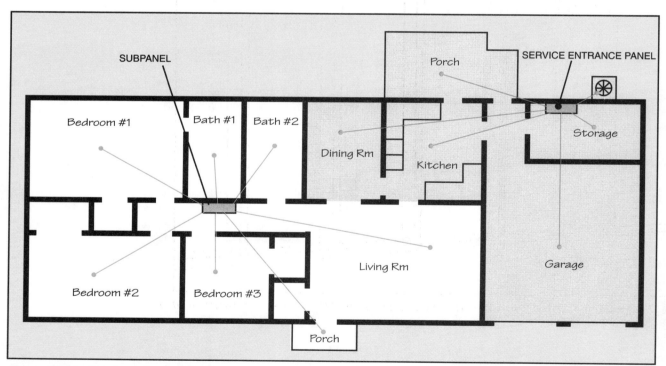

Figure 3-A-1. *Service entrance panels must be located near the service entrance. Subpanels are usually centrally located to help reduce long circuit runs.*

Locating and Marking SEP & Subpanel Locations

- Locate the position of the SEP and subpanel on the wiring plan and on the stud wall of the construction framework where it will be installed.

- Mark the location on the stud wall using a pencil or crayon. The bottom edge of the panel cabinets should be marked approximately **40** to **48** inches above the floor level or as required by local building codes **(Figure 3-A-2)**.

  Both the SEP and or subpanel may be installed as either surface or flush mounted as required by the wiring plan or building code regulations.

Figure 3-A-2. *Service entrance panels and subpanels should be located approximately 40 to 48 inches above the floor.*

B. Outlet Spacing Requirements

After marking the location of the SEP and subpanel, the next step will be to locate and mark the locations for the wall receptacles and switch outlets for the different branch circuits in the system. The NEC® general provisions state that in every kitchen, family room, dining room, parlor, library, den, sun room, bedroom, recreation room, or similar room, receptacle outlets shall adhere to spacing requirements. Check with your local building inspection office and the consult the proper **NEC®** reference for the required number and measurement spacing for all dwelling receptacle outlets.

■ Overhead Lighting Outlets

Overhead lighting outlets may be placed at the discretion of the architect or home owner depending on the desired aesthetic and functional results. However, most single overhead lighting outlets for room lighting are usually positioned in the middle of the room. **Figure 3-B-1** below shows an easy method of locating the center of a room ceiling.

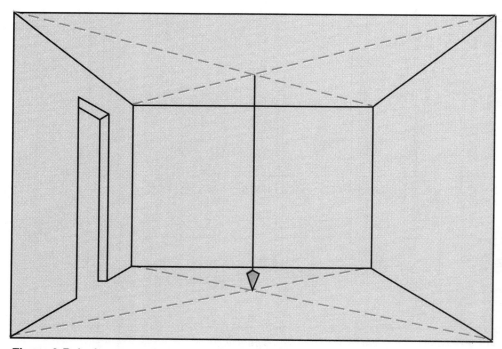

Figure 3-B-1. *An easy technique for locating the center of a room.*

■ Wall Outlets (Receptacles)

The NEC® requires wall receptacle outlets to be located so that no point along an **unbroken** wall measures greater than **6 feet** between outlets **(Figure 3-B-2)**. This includes any wall space of **2 feet** or more in width. Wall space is defined as a wall unbroken by doorways, fireplaces or similar openings. This requirement applies to rooms such as dining rooms, living rooms, bedrooms, etc. Each wall space **2 feet** wide or more shall be treated individually and separately from other wall spaces within the room.

 The NEC® does not a require a specific height for receptacle installations. The customary, accepted height for most wall receptacle installations is between **12 and 16 inches** above floor level **(Figure 3-B-3)**.

NEC® References For more on wall outlet spacing requirements, see NEC® Article 210-52

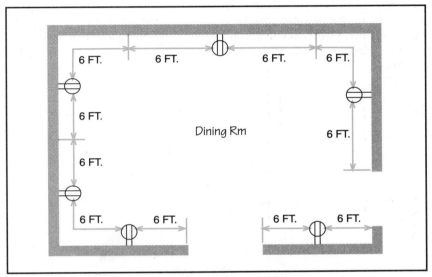

Figure 3-B-2. *The distance between wall outlets must meet NEC® minimum requirements.*

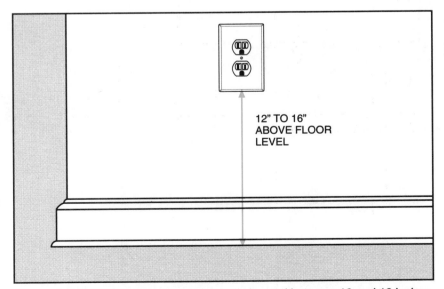

Figure 3-B-3. *Wall receptacles are typically located between 12 and 16 inches above the floor level.*

■ Kitchen Countertop Outlets (Receptacles)

The NEC® requires that kitchen countertop receptacles be installed at each counter space wider than **12 inches**. A counter space **12 inches** wide or wider is required to have a least (1) receptacle. Kitchen islands and/or peninsular counter tops **12 inches** wide or wider must have at least one (1) receptacle for each four **4 feet** of counter top.

Kitchen countertop receptacles must be installed so that no distance along a wall line is more than **24 inches** measured horizontally from a receptacle outlet in that space **(Figure 3-B-4).**

Receptacles intended to serve the counter top surfaces shall be located not more that **18 inches** above the countertop **(Figure 3-B-5)**

NEC® References
For more on kitchen outlet spacing, see NEC® Articles
210-52
210-52e

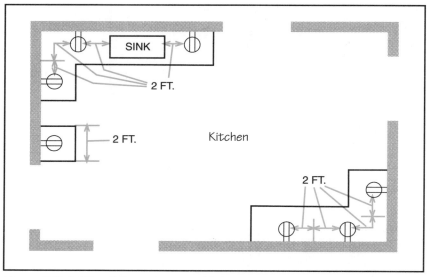

Figure 3-B-4. *The distance between kitchen countertop receptacles must meet NEC® minimum requirments.*

Author's Note:
All kitchen countertop receptacles must be GFCI protected.

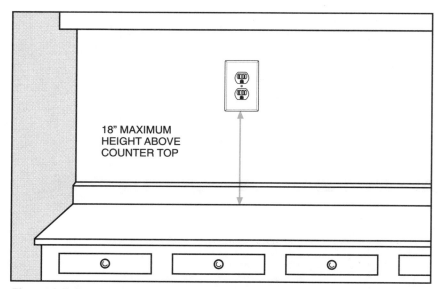

Figure 3-B-5. *Kitchen countertop receptacles must not be located more than 18 inches above the countertop.*

■ Closet and Storage Lighting Outlets

When planning overhead lighting outlets in clothes closets and storage areas, the NEC® requires specific measurements for locating **incandescent** and **fluorescent** fixtures. **Surface mounted incandescent** fixtures installed in closets must have at least **12 inches** between the fixture and the storage area **(Figure 3-B-6)**. **Surface mounted fluorescent** fixtures may be mounted within **6 inches** of the storage area **(Figure 3-B-7)**. Both fluorescent and incandescent **recessed fixtures** may be mounted on the ceiling or wall of the closet within **6 inches** between the fixture and the storage area. Both fixture types must be enclosed.

NEC® References
For more on closet and storage lighting outlet requirements, see NEC® Article 410-8

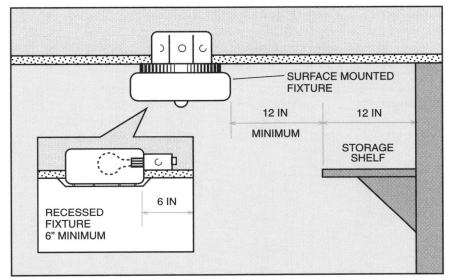

Figure 3-B-6. *Spacing requirements for surface mounted and recessed incandescent lighting fixtures installed in a closet or storage area.*

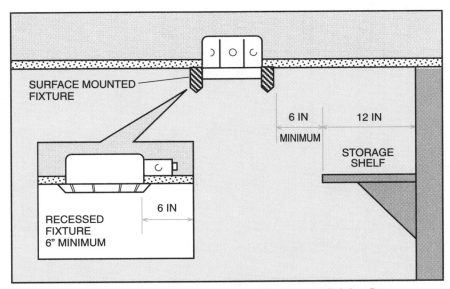

Figure 3-B-7. *Surfaced mounted and recessed fluorescent lighting fixtures may be located within 6 inches of storage shelf surfaces.*

C. Marking Outlets for a Circuit Run

To keep the different branch circuits separated for when planning and installing, always designate each circuit with a code number.

Small Appliance Circuit #1 on the plan could be coded **"SA1.** The letters **"S"** and **"A"** represent the circuit type, in this case, **Small Appliance.** The no. **"1"** indicates it is the first of two or more small appliance circuits.

The location of each outlet on the circuit should also be identified and marked. Example: SA1-**1**, SA1-**2**, SA1-**3**,

General Purpose Circuit #1 might be designated by the letters **"GP1."** Outlets on this circuit would be marked as **GP1-1, GP1-2, GP1-3**, etc. until all outlets on the circuit have been identified and marked. Repeat this procedure for each circuit on the plan until each outlet has been identified and marked on both the wiring plan and framework of the structure.

It is common practice to mark each receptacle location on the framework with a crayon or pencil. The receptacle location should be clearly marked at the correct height it is to be installed **(Figure 3 -C-1)**. Experienced installers sometimes use the length of a hammer handle as a quick measure for the correct height.

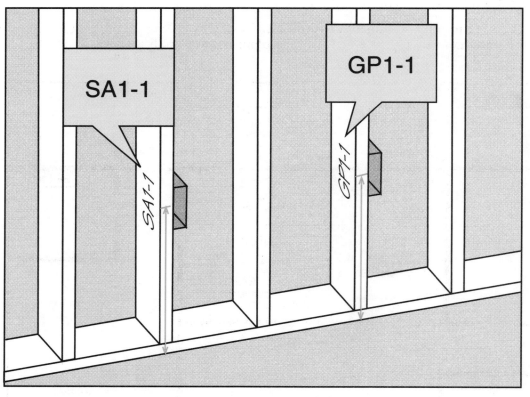

Figure 3-C-1. *Mark receptacle locations at the proper installation height.*

D. Planning Small Appliance Branch Circuits

When planning small appliance circuits, first determine the number of circuits necessary to meet the wiring plan requirements. The NEC® requires a minimum of 2 small appliance circuits in a single family residence. However, in larger homes, additional small appliance circuits may be added. The sample house wiring plan indicates the minimum two small appliance circuits. Both circuits begin in the service entrance panel located in the storage room.

Figure 3-D-1 illustrates the two small appliance circuits on the sample wiring plan and how you might choose to create the circuit runs for each.

Small appliance circuit #1, labeled as **SA1**, contains a total of **(7) outlets,** 2 of which are to be installed in the kitchen while 5 are to be installed in the dining room. Mark the first outlet nearest the SEP as **SA1-1** and continue to follow the wiring plan until all outlets on the circuit have been identified and marked: **SA12,SA1-3, SA1-4, SA1-5, SA1-6** and **SA1-7.**

Small appliance circuit #2 , labeled **SA2**, contains a total of **(5)** outlets, all of which are located in the kitchen. Mark the first outlet nearest the SEP as **SA2-1** and continue the marking sequence until all outlets and identified and labeled: **SA2-2, SA2-3, SA2-4** and **SA2-5**

Remember to consider the NEC® minimum and maximum spacing requirements for kitchen counter top receptacles when planning the small appliance circuits.

Author's Note: Although the NEC® requires only 2 small appliance circuits, larger homes may require additional small appliance circuits.

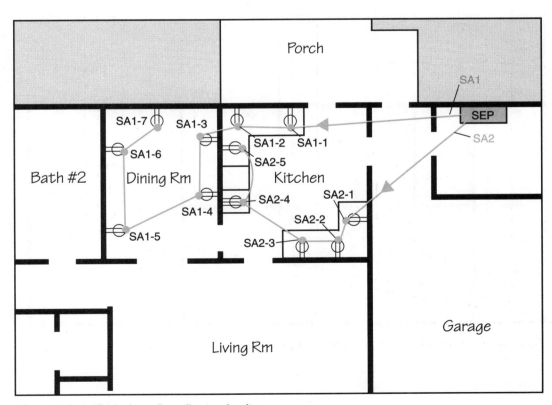

Figure 3-D-1. *Typical small appliance circuits.*

E. Planning General Purpose Branch Circuits

As described earlier in chapter two, general purpose circuits make up the largest portion of the home wiring system. General purpose circuits include all ceiling and wall mounted lighting outlets and most receptacles— other than those found in individual and small appliance or circuits designed for a specfic purpose. **Figure 3-E-1** below shows the general purpose circuits for our sample wiring plan. The process for marking general purpose circuits is made exactly like those just discussed for small appliance circuits except general purpose circuits will be marked as **GP (General Purpose)**

You must also mark the location of the switches that control the lighting and certain appliances. As stated in the introduction to this chapter, switch locations are indicated on the plan by a dotted line running from the switch to the outlet it controls. It is important for you to understand that once the circuit originates in the SEP or subpanel, it may then be routed to a receptacle, lighting outlet, appliance or to a switch to continue the circuit run (see wiring plan below).

A **switch leg** is necessary when the power source cable originates at an outlet box other than the switch box location. A switch leg is utilized to bring power from the outlet box (ie, lighting fixture, appliance, etc) to the switch that controls it. You will notice that the wiring plan includes the symbols **S** (single-pole switches) **S₃** (three-way switches) and **S₄** (four-way switches). These symbols represent the locations of the wall switches that control the room lighting.

NEC® References For more on general purpose circuits, see NEC® Articles: 100 210

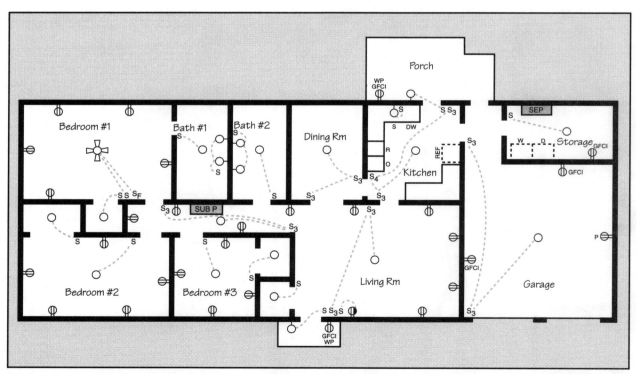

Figure 3-E-1. *The sample wiring plan showing general branch circuits and switch locations.*

Calculating the Required Number of General Purpose Circuits

How do you determine the number of general purpose circuits you will need for a residence? This is an important question that must be answered if the residential wiring system is to be properly installed. The NEC® provides detailed procedures for computing the required number of general purpose circuits.

The general rule for estimating the number of circuits is that a minimum of one **(1)** general purpose circuit be required for every **500 square feet** of floor space. Assuming our sample house plan has **2500 square foot**, the plan would call for **five (5)** general purpose circuits. You may use more circuits than called for with this formula, but you must never use less.

2500 divided by 500 = 5

Most house plans will show the square footage of the house on the plan. If not, it can be easily calculated by multiplying the outside dimensions of the plan, excluding open porches and garages.

For example: a two - story house plan measures 28 ft. X 40 ft on each floor.

28 ft. X 40 ft. = 1120 square feet per floor

1120 X 2 floors = 2240 square feet

To find the required number of general purpose circuits for 2240 square feet of floor space:

Divide 2240 by 500. This equals **4.48** general purpose circuits. Always go to the next highest number if the division ends in a fraction. This means the total number of general purpose circuits required for 2240 square feet of floor space is **5**.

You will want to include areas which might be developed for future use such as unfinished attics or basements. If these areas exist in future plans, you will want to plan at least one **(1)** general purpose circuit for these areas. If the area is to be used for storage or contains equipment that will require periodic service, you should provide at least one **(1)** outlet in the circuit.

Table 3-1 General Purpose Circuit Totals (Based on sample floor plan)		
Location	**Lighting Outlets**	**Receptacle Outlets**
Bedroom #1	1	5
Closet	1	0
Bedroom #2	1	5
Closet	1	0
Bedroom #3	1	4
Closet	1	0
Hallway	1	4
Front Porch	1	1 (GFCI)
Rear Porch	1	1 (GFCI)
Bath #1	3	3 (GFCI)
Bath #2	3	3 (GFCI)
Living Room	1	6
Foyer Closet	1	0
Garage	1	3 (GFCI)
Storage	1	1 (GFCI)
Total	**19**	**36**
Total Outlets for all General Purpose Circuits **55**		

Note: Outlets for kitchen, dining room, laundry and all individual circuits are not included in total.

Calculating the Number of Outlets in Each Circuit

Your next step is to determine how many outlets will be installed on each circuit. It is desirable — and practical—to divide the outlets evenly among the circuits whenever possible. But it may prove difficult to have the same number of outlets on each circuit. Some circuits will have more— some less.

Some rooms may have part of their outlets on one circuit and part on another. This may be necessary to balance the current load properly and is desirable when planning the circuit run. When planning circuits, keep in mind those combinations that will require the least amount of electrical cable installation.

Below is a simple procedure that can be used to help you determine how to balance the load on general purpose circuits.

1. Assume that all general purpose circuits are rated at 20-amperes. Include in your count all ceiling and wall lighting outlets and all convenience outlets.

    Do not include outlets for small appliance, individual or laundry in your count.

2. Review the outlet totals in **Table 3-1 (page 40)**. The numbers in this table are based on the information illustrated in the sample wiring plan.

3. Add together the total number of ceiling and wall lighting outlets in column 1 and the number of receptacle outlets in column 2.

4. We have already determined that our sample house plan has 2500 square foot house and will require a minimum of five **(5)** general purpose circuits. Divide the total number of general purpose outlets **(55)** by the required minimum number of general purpose circuits **(5)**.

    55 outlets divided by 5 general purpose circuits = 11 outlets per circuit.

    You will notice that our wiring plan example uses 6 general purpose circuits. In this case, 55 divided by 6 equals 9 outlets per circuit. This number is well within the average number of 13 outlets allowable per 20-ampere circuit.

NEC® References
For more on calculating the number of outlets on a circuit, see NEC® Articles 220-2 220-3 220-4

Author's Note:
Do not exceed 10 outlets for each 15-ampere general purpose circuit or 13 outlets for each 20-ampere general purpose circuit.

1.5 Amps per outlet

Intermittant use = continuous use

Switch Leg = #12 wire = brings power from outlet to switch

all switch Box 42" to Top

■ Planning General Purpose Circuit # 1 (GP1)

General Purpose Circuit #1 begins in the SEP.

Using the sample house wiring plan **(Figure 3-E-2)**, you can now plan general purpose circuit #1. First, determine the number of outlets to be served on the circuit. You can see by looking at the sample wiring plan that five **(5)** outlets are to be served. This total includes three **(3)** wall outlets, two **(2)** lighting outlets with their switch legs. This circuit will supply power to:

1. **Storage Room:** overhead lighting and switch outlet and and one (1) wall receptacle.

2. **Garage:** wall receptacles, overhead lighting and switch outlets.

- Start with the storage room outlet nearest the SEP and label it **GP1-1**.

- Label the storage room lighting outlet and switch leg **GP1-2** .

- Next, move to the nearest receptacle in the garage area and label it **GP1-3.**

- Label the next wall receptacle in the garage as **GP1-4.**

- Finally, label the overhead garage lighting and three-way switch outlets as **GP1-5**

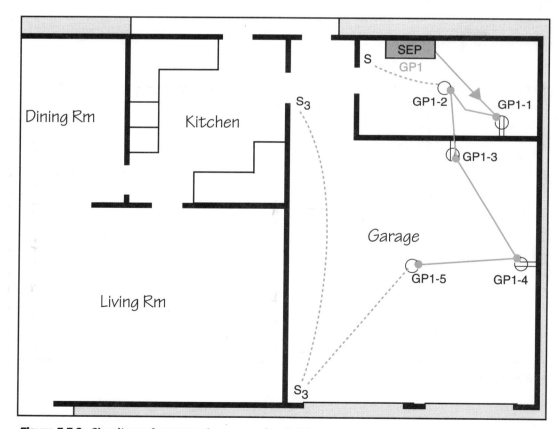

Figure 3-E-2. *Circuit run for general purpose circuit #1.*

■ Planning General Purpose Circuit #2 (GP2)

General Purpose Circuit #2 begins in the SEP.

General purpose circuit #2, **Figure 3-E-3,** consists of three **(3)** lighting outlets and their switch legs and one **(1)** weather-protected GFCI receptacle. This circuit supplies electrical power to:

1. **Kitchen:** overhead lighting and three-way and four-way switch outlets.

2. **Back Porch:** weather-protected GFCI receptacle, porch lighting and switch outlets.

- Begin this circuit at the ceiling lighting and switch outlets in the kitchen and label them **GP2-1.**

- Label the next lighting and switch outlet over the kitchen sink **GP2-2.**

- Label the weather-protected GFCI on the porch **GP2-3.**

- Label the back porch lighting and switch outlets **GP2-4.**

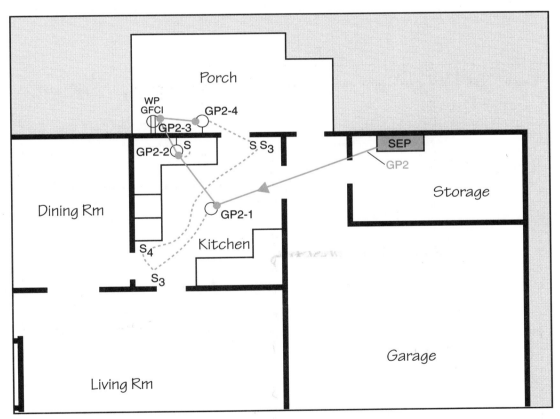

Figure 3-E-3. *Circuit run for general purpose circuit #2.*

Planning General Purpose Circuit # 3 (GP3)

General Purpose Circuit #3 begins in the hall subpanel.

General purpose circuit #3 (**Figure 3-E-4**) consists of six (**6**) wall outlets and six (**6**) lighting outlets with their switch legs for the following rooms:

1. **Hallway:** overhead lighting and switch outlets and wall receptacles.

2. **Bathroom #2:** overhead lighting and switch outlets and wall lighting.

3. **Bedroom #3:** overhead lighting and switch outlets, closet lighting and switch outlets and wall receptacles.

4. **Front entrance closet:** overhead lighting and lighting switch leg.

- Starting at the subpanel, mark the **loca**tion for the nearest wall receptacle and label it **GP3-1**.

- Label the overhead hall lighting and three-way switch outlets **GP3-2**. Mark the locations for the two switches as **S**$_3$.

- Label the hallway receptacle outlets nearest the bedrooms **GP3-3 and GP3-4**.

- Moving to bedroom #3, label the two wall receptacles **GP3-5 and GP3-6**. Label the lighting and switch outlets for the adjacent closets, **GP3-7** and **GP3-8**.

- Moving from **GP3-4** in the hallway, label the last receptacle outlet **GP3-9**. Label the overhead lighting and switch outlets in bathroom #2, **GP3-10, GP3-11 and GP3-12**.

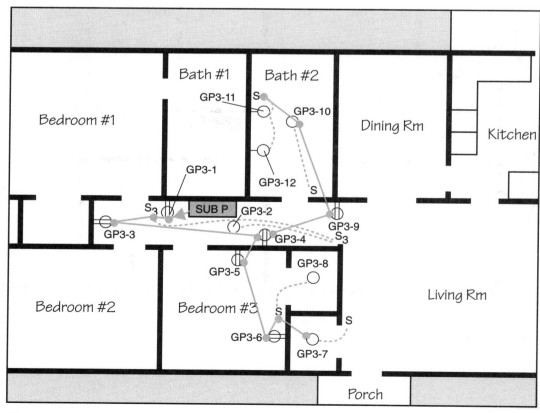

Figure 3-E-4 *Circuit run for general purpose circuit #3.*

Planning General Purpose Circuit #4 (GP4)

General Purpose Circuit #4 begins in the hall subpanel.

General purpose circuit #4 **(Figure 3-E-5)** consists of five **(5)** wall outlets, six **(6)** lighting outlets and their switch legs and is designed to serve:

1. **Bathroom #1:** wall receptacles, lighting and switch outlets.

2. **Bedroom #1:** wall receptacles, lighting and switch outlets It also serves a fan lighting and switch outlets.

- Beginning at the subpanel, label the ceiling and switch outlets in bathroom #2 as **GP4-1**. Label both wall lighting and switch outlets **GP4-2 and GP4-3**.

- Next, label the first wall receptacle in bedroom#1.

- Continue labeling each wall receptacle around the room until each is consecutively labeled **GP4-5, GP4-6, GP4-7** and **GP4-8.**

- Label the closet lighting and switch outlets **GP4-9.**

- Label the fan/lighting and switch outlets **GP4-10.** Label the switch leg for the light **S** and the switch leg for the fan S_F.

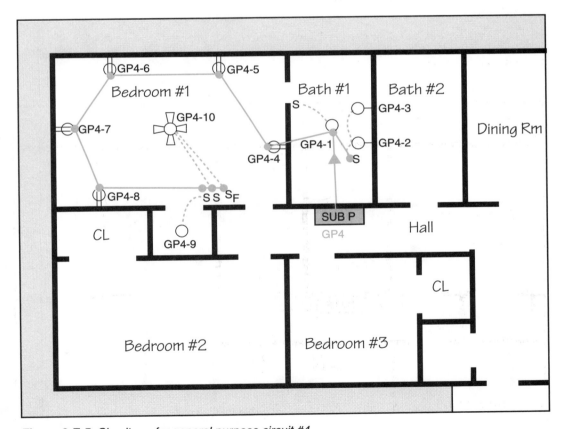

Figure 3-E-5 *Circuit run for general purpose circuit #4.*

■ Planning General Purpose Circuit #5 (GP5)

General Purpose Circuit #5 begins in the hall subpanel.

General purpose circuit #5 **(Figure 3-E-6)** consists of wall and lighting outlets in the following rooms:

1. **Bedroom #3:** lighting and wall receptacles

2. **Bedroom #2:** lighting and wall receptacles.

- Beginning in bedroom #3 label the first wall receptacle **GP5-1**.

- Label the overhead room lighting and switch outlets **GP5-2**.

- Label the remaining wall receptacle **GP5-3**.

- Move to bedroom #2 and mark the wall outlets **GP5-4, GP5-5, GP5-6**.

- Mark the overhead closet lighting and switch outlet **GP5-7**.

- Mark the next wall outlet as **GP5-8** and the overhead lighting outlet and switch outlet **GP5-9**.

- Mark the last wall outlet in bedroom #2 **GP5-10**.

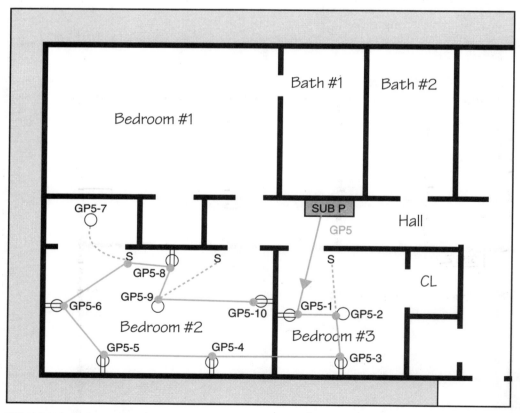

Figure 3-E-6 *Circuit run for general purpose circuit #5.*

■ Planning General Purpose Circuit #6 (GP6)

General Purpose Circuit #6 begins in the hall subpanel.

General purpose circuit #6 **(Figure 3-E-7)** consists of eight **(8)** wall receptacles, three **(3)** lighting outlets and their switch legs. Circuit #6 serves:

1. **Living Room:** lighting and three-way switch outlets. It also includes wall receptacles including a split-receptacle with switch leg.

2. **Dining Room**: lighting and three-way switch outlets.

3. **Front Porch**: lighting and switch outlet and outdoor GFCI weather-proof receptacle.

4. **Garage**: GFCI receptacle.

- Label the first living room receptacle **GP6-1 and** the dining room lighting and three-way switch outlets **GP6-2.**

- Next, label the porch lighting outlet and switch leg **GP6-3 and the GFCI** weather-proof porch receptacle **GP6-4.**

- Label the living room overhead lighting and three-way switch outlets **GP6-5.**

- Label the split-wired receptacle and switch outlet **GP6-6.** Note that the split-wired outlet is identified by a different receptacle symbol.

- Label the remaining receptacle outlets in the living room and the GFCI protected outlet in the garage: **GP6-7, GP6-8, GP6-9 (GFCI), GP6-10** and **GP6-11.**

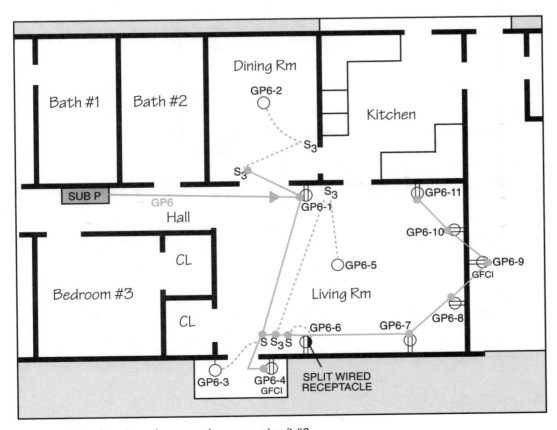

Figure 3-E-7. *Circuit run for general purpose circuit #6.*

F. Planning Individual Branch Circuits

The NEC® requires that individual circuits be installed to serve appliances and other equipment that require more power to operate than do small appliance and general purpose circuits. This means that each appliance, or piece of equipment, must be supplied by a separate circuit cable from the SEP or subpanel. Wiring an appliance directly to the SEP without the use of a receptacle and plug assembly is also called **hardwiring**. Some circuits are connected directly—or **hardwired**—from the service panel to the appliance while others are connected using a receptacle and plug-and-cord assembly.

Author's Note: While not required by the NEC®, it is good practice to install refrigerators and freezers on individual circuits.

Most small appliance and general purpose circuits operate at 120-volts. Individual circuits that serve large equipment usually require 240-volts or a combination of 120/240-volts.

Large appliances and equipment typically requiring individual circuits are dishwashers, trash compactors, water heaters, furnaces, heat pumps, ranges, separate ovens, clothes dryers and clothes washers. **Table 3-2** below offers a quick reference for recommended voltages, cable/conductor sizes and overcurrent protection for individual circuits.

Note that all individual circuits shown on **Figure 3-F-1** are served from the SEP with the exception of two heater circuits in bathrooms #1 and #2.

Table 3-2 Recommended Voltage, Conductor Size and Overcurrent Protection Ratings for Individual Branch Circuits			
Circuit	**Voltage**	**Conductor Size (Copper)**	**Circuit Breaker (Amps)**
Air Conditioner (large)	240	12	20
Water Heater	240	10	20/30
Separate Ovens	120/240	10	30
Counter Cooktop	120/240	10	30
Clothes Dryer	120/240	10	30
Range (self contained)	120/240	6	50
Central Air/Heat Pump	240	8/6	40/60
Water Pump	240	12	20
Furnace	240	6	50

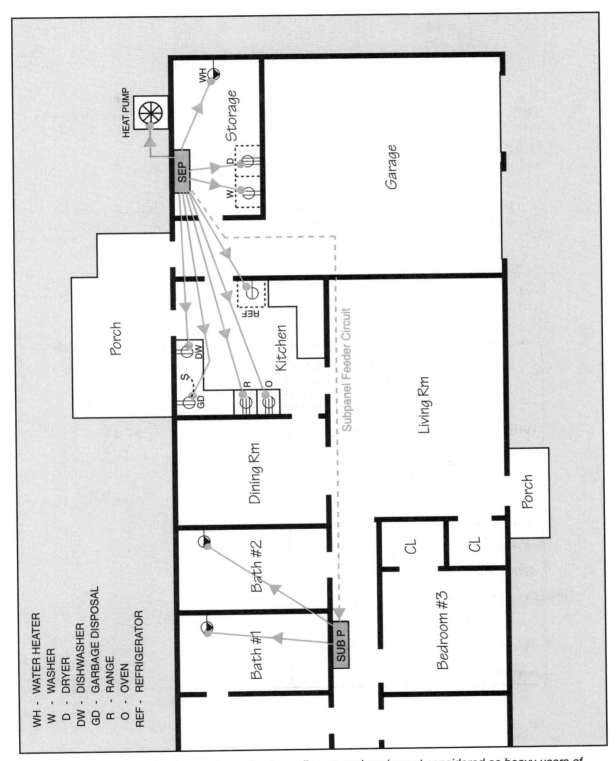

Figure 3-F-1. *Individual circuits supply service to appliances and equipment considered as heavy users of electric power.*

G. Planning Bathroom Branch Circuits

Bathrooms are defined by the NEC® as any area having a basin and one or more toilet, tub or shower. The NEC® requires separate branch circuits for bathrooms. These circuits are to serve <u>only</u> those outlets in bathrooms. No other outlet may be connected to these circuits. Circuits must have 20-ampere overcurrent protection and each outlet must be GFCI protected.

NEC® References
For more on
bathroom
circuit
requirements, see
NEC® Article
210-52d

The NEC® will permit a single 20-ampere circuit to serve two bathrooms. However, with today's lifestyles focusing more activity in bathrooms and dressing areas, separate circuits installed for each bathroom is a better arrangement **(Figure 3-G-1).**

- The bathroom circuits on the sample wiring plan are served from the hall subpanel. Circuit designations are labeled **BA1** and **BA2**.

- The outlets on bathroom circuit #1 are labeled **BA1-1**, **BA1-2** and **BA1-3**. As required by the NEC®, the first outlet in the circuit must be a GFCI outlet.

- The outlets for bathroom circuit #2 are labeled **BA2-1**, **BA2-2** and **BA2-3**.

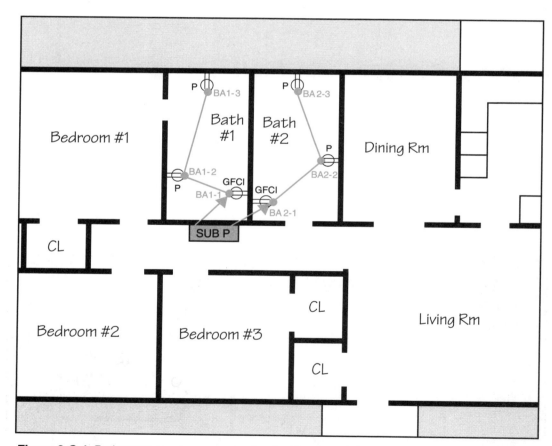

Figure 3-G-1. *Bathrooms require separate circuits. No other outlets may be included on these circuits.*

Electrical Boxes

All electrical connections in a residential wiring system must be contained in approved **device** or **outlet boxes**. These boxes are designed to prevent electrical sparks from igniting the wood framing materials in the structure or other flammable items within the walls of the dwelling. **Device boxes** are generally defined as either rectangular or square boxes that contain switches and/ or receptacles and circuit cables/conductors **(Figure 4-1)**. They are also called **switch boxes**. Device boxes used for switches and duplex receptacles are usually rectangular.

Outlet and junction boxes are commonly defined as boxes that will contain conductor/cable connections for ceiling and wall lighting fixtures or connections for large appliances **(Figure 4-2)**. They are usually round, octagonal or square-shaped and are larger than the typical rectangular shaped device boxes. They are usually used where more space is needed inside the box to make multiple wiring connections.

NEC® References
For more on device and outlet boxes, see NEC® Article 370

In this chapter, you will learn the different types of device and outlet boxes commonly used in the wiring installation and how to select and properly install the right box for the right job.

Topics discussed are:

A. Nonmetallic Device Boxes

B. Metallic Device Boxes

C. Installing Device Boxes

D. Outlet and Junction Boxes

E. Electrical Box Size Requirements

Figure 4-1. *A nonmetallic device box typically used for switch and receptacle installations.*

Figure 4-2. *A metallic outlet box installed for a ceiling lighting fixture.*

A. Nonmetallic Device Boxes

Nonmetallic device boxes have quickly become the industry choice for wiring residential buildings and are most common in new construction installations. They are lightweight, durable, easily installed and come in a variety of shapes and sizes for most applications. They are also inexpensive when compared to metallic boxes of the same type and size. Materials used for these boxes may be plastic, PVC or fiberglass. Nonmetallic boxes may be used **only** with nonmetallic sheathed cable.

Device boxes can be purchased in a variety of common sizes and styles **(Figure 4-A-1)**. The most common (2-inch by 3-inch), nonmetallic boxes include nails used to install the box to the house framework. A newer type of nonmetallic device box is equipped with an adjusting screw that allows the electrician to set the box either in or out for proper depth alignment **(Figure 4-A-2)**. For more information on nonmetallic box requirements, consult the NEC®.

*NEC® References
For more on
nonmetallic device
boxes, see
NEC® Articles
300
370-17c*

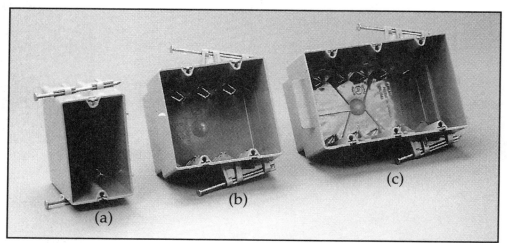

Figure 4-A-1. *Examples of common nonmetallic device boxes. (a) Single device box. (b) Double-gang box. (c) Triple-gang box*

Figure 4-A-2. *Examples of nonmetallic device boxes used in special applications.*

Another important factor that has contributed to the popularity of nonmetallic boxes is that cable clamps are not required inside the box **(Figure 4-A-3)**. This greatly increases the available space inside the box making it easier and faster for the electrical installer to make conductor connections. However, some new variations of the nonmetallic box come equipped with cable clamps, such as the depth adjusting box shown in **(Figure 4-A-4)**.

Cables enter the box through holes called **knockouts** or **pryouts** located in pairs at the top and bottom rear of the box **(Figure 4-A-5)**. They are easily removed with a screwdriver **(Figure 4-A-6).**

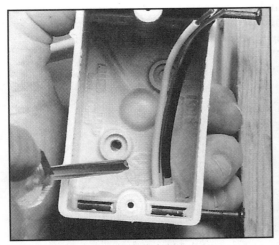

Figure 4-A-3. *Nonmetallic device boxes do not require cable clamps.*

Figure 4-A-4. *Some newer types of nonmetallic device boxes also contain cable clamps.*

Figure 4-A-5. *Knockouts permit electrical cable access into the nonmetallic device boxes.*

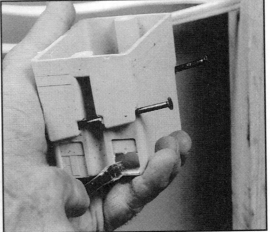

Figure 4-A-6. *Knockouts in nonmetallic device boxes are easily removed with a screwdriver.*

B. Metallic Device Boxes

Metallic device boxes for many years were the standard for most wiring installations. But the increased popularity of nonmetallic boxes has diminished their use in residential wiring installations. Metal boxes may still be used in residential wiring applications, however they are most often used in commercial wiring installations and for special applications within the residential wiring such as mounting ceiling fans or as required by the NEC® or local codes.

Metallic boxes, like nonmetallic boxes, come in a variety of shapes and sizes for most all wiring applications. Some of the more popular sizes and styles are shown below in **Figures 4-B-1 and 4-B-2**.

NEC® References
For more on
metallicdevice
boxes, see
NEC® Articles
370
370-4
370-27

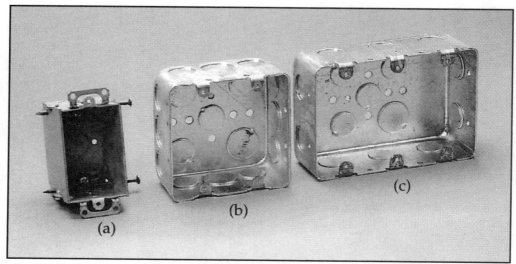

Figure 4-B-1. *Examples of typical metallic device boxes. (a) Single box. (b) Double-gang box. (c) Triple-gang box.*

Figure 4-B-2. *Examples of metallic device boxes for special applications.*

Metal boxes differ from nonmetallic boxes, not only in the materials from which they are constructed, but also in their features and requirements for installation. Special features of metallic device boxes are shown below in **Figure 4-B-3.**

- **Mounting Ears -** make mounting and adjusting the box easier during installation. They are especially useful when installation is required in an existing home but are also used in new construction.

- **Device Mounts -** used for securing devices (switches and receptacles) to the box.

- **Grounding Screw -** A grounding screw is available for installation in metal boxes and used for securing the equipment grounding conductor to the metal box. The NEC® requires that all cables and devices installed in a metal device box must be securely grounded to the box.

- **Knockouts -** coin-sized plugs located on the sides, back, and bottom of a metal box. When removed, the knockout provides an opening through which electrical cables enter and exit the box.

- **Pryouts -** located in pairs at the rear, top and bottom of the box. Pryouts provide access to the box for installing electrical cable.

- **Cable Clamps -** required in metallic boxes for securing cable to the box. Boxes may be purchased with or without cable clamps.

Author's Note:
When installing NM cable in a metal box, cable clamps must be used to secure the cable in the box.

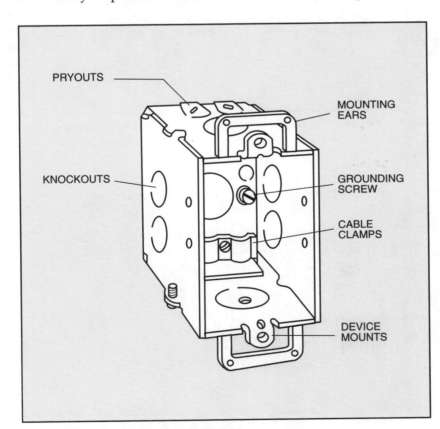

Figure 4-B-3. *Parts of a metallic device box.*

Other special features of metallic device boxes are:

- **Jumper Grounding Conductors (also called Pigtails)** - sometimes provided with metal device boxes. This simple device, shown here installed with a grounding screw, saves time for the installer when connecting the cables or devices in the box **(Figure 4-B-4)**.

- **Cable Clamps** - required when using metal device and outlet boxes to secure the cable within the box **(Figure 4-B-5)**.

- **Cable Connectors** - required to secure cables at their entry point in the box when knockouts are utilized **(Figure 4-B-6)**.

- **Grounding Clips** may also be used for making the equipment ground to a metallic box **(Figure 4-B-7)**.

NEC® Reference
For more on grounding metallic device boxes see NEC® Article 250-74

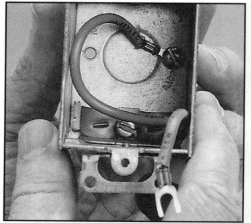

Figure 4-B-4. *The NEC® requires pigtails (jumper grounding conductors) to be installed when using metallic device boxes.*

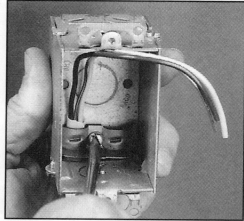

Figure 4-B-5. *Cable clamps are required in all metallic device and outlet boxes.*

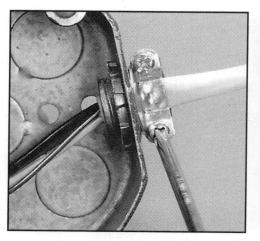

Figure 4-B-6. *Cable connectors are required on metallic device boxes to secure cables at their point of entry into the box.*

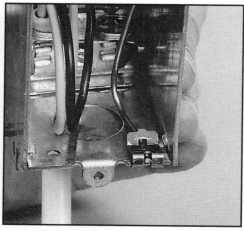

Figure 4-B-7. *Grounding clips may be used when securing the equipment grounding conductor to the box.*

C. Installing Device Boxes

Device boxes and outlet boxes— both nonmetallic and metallic— must be installed in compliance with NEC® requirements.

It requires that when the finished surface of a limited-combustible or noncombustible wall is plaster, concrete or gypsum wallboard (sheetrock), boxes must be mounted not more than 1/4 -inch in back of the finished surface **(Figure 4-C-1)**. On walls constructed of combustible materials such as solid wood or wood paneling, boxes must be mounted flush with the edge of the wall surface **(Figure 4-C-2)**.

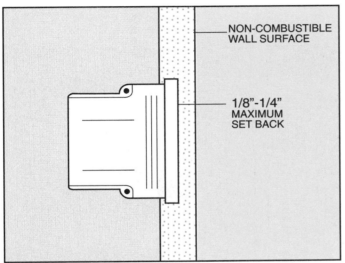

Figure 4-C-1. *Device boxes must be installed not more than 1/4 - inch in back of a noncombustible, finished wall surface.*

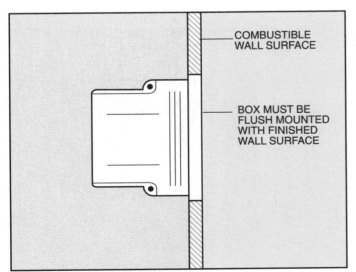

Figure 4-C-2. *Device boxes must be mounted flush with the finished surface of walls constructed of combustible materials.*

NEC® References
For more on installing device boxes see NEC® Articles
370-19
370-20
370-21

■ Installing Nonmetallic Boxes

The most common method for installing nonmetallic boxes is by nailing them directly to the wood framing. **Figure 4-C-3** illustrates a box equipped with nails ready for installation. They are also available with side-mounting brackets which are nailed or screwed to the surface of the stud **(Figure 4-C-4)**. Some boxes are made with depth gauge marks while others are equipped with depth indicator tabs on the side of the box **(Figure 4-C-5)**. These aid in installing the box at the required depth.

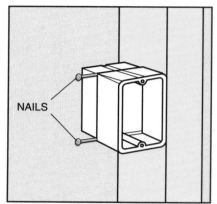

Figure 4-C-3. *Nonmetallic boxes installed using nails.*

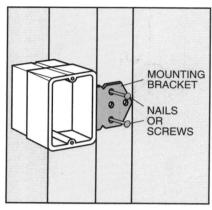

Figure 4-C-4. *Box installed with a side-mounting bracket.*

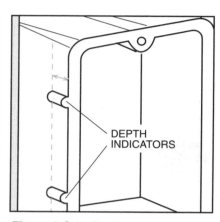

Figure 4-C-5. *Depth gauge indicators on a device box.*

▲ Basic Steps for Installing a Nonmetallic Box

- First, determine where the cables will enter and exit the device box and open the pryouts with a screwdriver **(Figure 4-C-6)**.

- Next, determine the depth at which the box is to be installed on the stud. This depth will depend on the material used for the finished wall surface **(Figure 4-C-7)**.

- Finally, nail the box to the stud at the proper height and depth **(Figure 4-C-8)**.

Figure 4-C-6. *Open the pryout with a screwdriver.*

Figure 4-C-7. *Measure for the proper depth and height .*

Figure 4-C-8. *Nail the box to the stud.*

Installing Metallic Boxes

Both nonmetallic and metallic boxes are commonly installed by nailing or screwing them directly to the framing studs, joists or rafters **(Figure 4-C-9)**. They may also be mounted using side mounting brackets **(Figure 4-C-10)**. Metal boxes may come equipped with side depth gauge marks to assist the installer in setting the box at the correct depth on the stud **Figure 4-C-11)**.

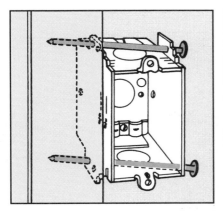

Figure 4-C-9. *Mounting a box with nails.*

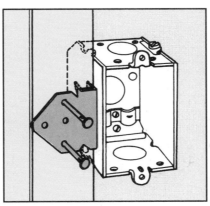

Figure 4-C-10. *Mounting with a mounting bracket.*

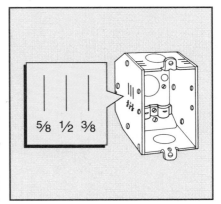

Figure 4-C-11. *Depth gauge markings on the box.*

▲ Basic Steps for Installing a Metallic Box

- Determine where the cables will enter and exit the box and remove the knockouts and/or pryouts. Remove only those knockouts necessary **(Figure 4-C-12)**.

- Based on the thickness of the material used for the finished wall surface, determine the mounting depth of the box **(Figure 4-C-13)**.

- Nail the box to the stud at the proper height using No. 10 galvanized nails **(Figure 4-C-14)**.

Figure 4-C-12. *Remove the pryout with a screwdriver.*

Figure 4-C-13. *Measure for height and finished surface exposure.*

Figure 4-C-14. *Nail the box to the stud at the selected height.*

■ Installing Boxes Between Studs

During the installation of a circuit run, you may discover that the wiring plan will require an outlet to be located between wall studs and ceiling joists rather than attached directly to the framework. This minor problem is easily solved by installing wooden or metal support strips between the studs and mounting the box on them. Wooden support strips can be easily made from strips of scrap lumber **(Figure 4-C-15)**. Metal supports, such as adjustable bar hangers, can be used and are available at electrical suppliers and home centers **(Figure 4-C-16)**.

Author's Note:
When using either of these methods, make sure the box will be flush with the finished wall surface.

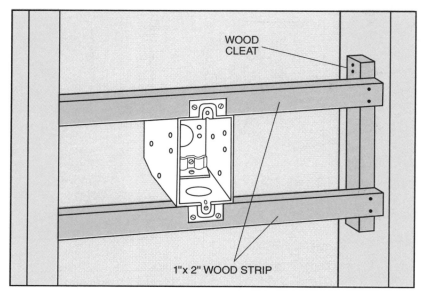

Figure 4-C-15. *Wooden cleats and strips may be used for mounting device boxes between studs.*

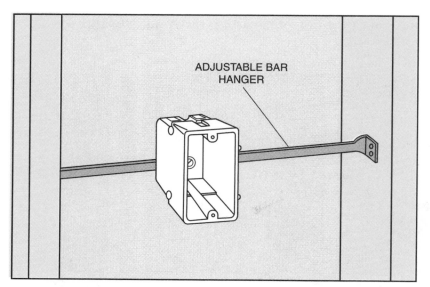

Figure 4-C-16. *Adjustable metal support brackets are also a common method for mounting boxes between studs.*

Installing Handy Boxes

Handy boxes, unlike regular device boxes, are designed to be mounted directly to the surface edge of a stud or wall. They are commonly used in areas such as garages, basements, utility buildings, service areas and agricultural applications.

▲ Mounting a handy box to a stud

- Position the box at the proper height.
- Attach the box to the stud with nails or woodscrews **(Figure 4-C-17)**.

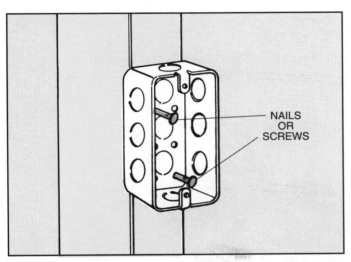

NAILS
OR
SCREWS

Figure 4-C-17. *Handy boxes may be mounted to the surface of a stud with nails or screws.*

▲ Mounting a handy box to a block surface

- Drill holes into the surface and install screw inserts **(Figure 4-C-18)**.
- Position the box and attach with screws.

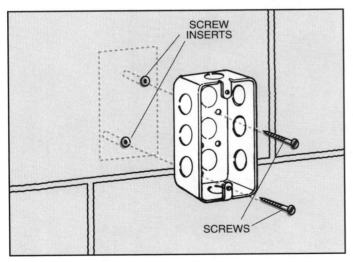

SCREW
INSERTS

SCREWS

Figure 4-C-18. *Mounting a handy box to a cement block surface using screws and screw inserts.*

D. Outlet & Junction Boxes

■ Outlet Boxes

An **outlet box** may be generally defined as one in which conductor connections are made when installing ceiling and wall lighting outlets and/ or connecting small and large appliance circuits. They are used for these installations because they are larger, come in a various shapes for a variety of special applications and provide more room for multiple wiring installations than do typical device boxes. **Figures 4-D-1** and **4-D-2** are typical examples of nonmetallic and metallic outlet boxes. The most common types of outlet boxes used for most residential installations are the round, octagonal and square shapes. Box covers—which are required by the NEC® for all installations—are available for all box sizes and shapes.

Devices such as switches and receptacles, while normally installed in device boxes, may also be installed in outlet boxes by using specially designed box covers.

NEC® References
For more on junction boxes, see NEC® Articles
300-15
300-16
370-23
370-29

Figure 4-D-1. *Examples of typical nonmetallic outlet boxes*

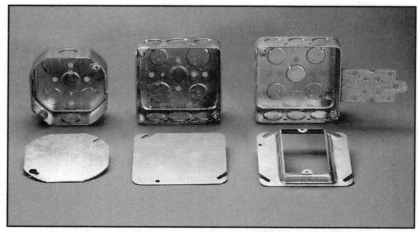

Figure 4-D-2. *Examples of typical metallic outlet boxes.*

Junction Boxes

Junction boxes are used where more capacity is required for making multiple connections. They are most often used when making connections for appliances such as water heaters, dishwashers, garbage disposals and other individual equipment circuits **(Figure 4-D-3)**. Special box covers are also available for installing switches or receptacles **(Figure 4-D-4)**. Typical junction box covers are usually round or octagonal but are also available in raised and flat device styles for switch and receptacle installations **(Figure 4-D-5)**. **Extension rings** may be added to give increased capacity to an existing junction box **(Figure 4-D-6)**.

Junction boxes are required to be accessible without altering the finish of the building. Attics, garages, crawl spaces underneath the dwelling and unfinished basements are typical areas where they are commonly used. The NEC® offers specific requirements for installing junction boxes.

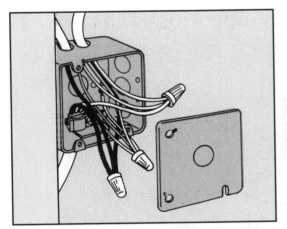

Figure 4-D-3. *Junction boxes are commonly used when making multiple wiring connections.*

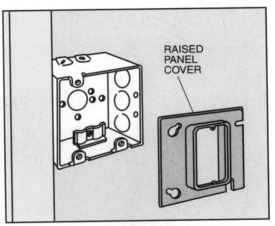

Figure 4-D-4. *A raised device box cover.*

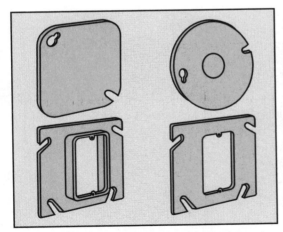

Figure 4-D-5. *Typical box covers for outlet and junction boxes.*

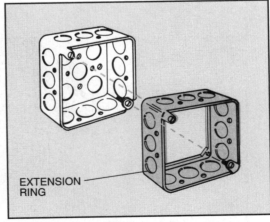

Figure 4-D-6. *Extension rings give added space to a junction box.*

■ Installing Outlet & Junction Boxes

Round or square nonmetallic boxes and octagonal or square metallic boxes, are commonly used for most residential lighting outlets. Square or round boxes are selected where additional space is required when making multiple conductor connections. As with any device box, knockouts must also be removed from outlet and junction boxes. **Figure 4-D-7** illustrates a common technique for removing knockouts from a metallic outlet box. Unused openings in both device boxes and outlet boxes must be plugged with a knockout seal **(Figure 4-D-8)**.

NEC® References
For more on
installing outlet
boxes, see
NEC® Articles
370-19
370-20
370-21

Junction and outlet boxes, like device boxes, are commonly installed to the framework using nails or screws. They may also be mounted by the following methods:

- Metal adjustable bar hangers

- Wooden supports made from scrap lumber

- Special support systems designed for heavy loads

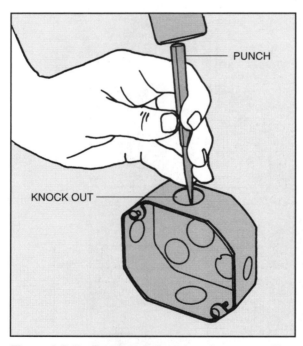

Figure 4-D-7. *Removing a knockout from a metallic box.*

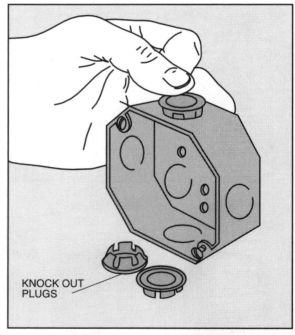

Figure 4-D-8. *Unused openings must be sealed with knockout seals,*

Installing Outlet Boxes Using Adjustable Bar Hangers

Outlet boxes used for installing overhead lighting are typically installed using **adjustable metal bar hangers** attached to ceiling joists.

Both nonmetallic and metallic boxes are available with adjustable bar hanger assemblies or may be purchased separately. They may be straight, offset, adjustable or solid and usually come in lengths of 18, 24, or 30 inches. To install a nonmetallic outlet box using an adjustable bar hanger:

- Assemble the outlet box to the adjustable hanger bar with the screws and fitting supplied with the bar. **(Figure 4-D-9a)**.

- Make sure the box surface is flush with the ceiling surface and tap the ends of the hanger bar into position between the joists with a hammer **(Figure 4-D-9b)**.

- Screw or nail the hanger bar to the joist **(Figure 4-D-9c)**.

- Move the box into the desired position between the joists and tighten the bar set screw firmly against the fitting **(Figure 4-D-9d)**.

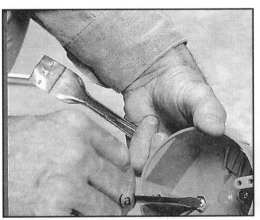
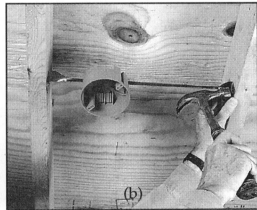

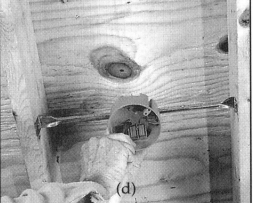

Author's Note: *Make sure the box is always flush with the finished ceiling or wall surface.*

Figure 4-D-9. *Installing a nonmetallic outlet box using an adjustable bar hanger.*

■ Installing Outlet Boxes With Scrap Lumber

One of the oldest, and still one of the most popular methods of installing ceiling outlet boxes is by using scrap lumber. All construction projects will have scrap lumber at the building site that must be discarded in some manner. A good—and inexpensive—use for scrap 2X4's and 2x6's is to use them to mount device and outlet boxes. Not only do you deplete the scrap pile, you also save money by removing the need to purchase more expensive adjustable metal bar hangers.

Cut the pieces so they will fit snugly between the studs or joists **(Figure 4-D-10)**. Once the required mounting height has been determined, secure the wood to the framework using nails or screws. Care should be exercised to ensure that the box surface will not extend beyond the finished surface of the ceiling or wall **(Figure 4-D-11)**.

Author's Note:
Be sure you mount the box in a manner that will allow access for installing the cable.

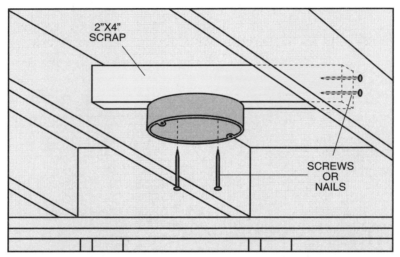

Figure 4-D-10. *Nail or screw pre-cut wooden scraps into position between ceiling joists.*

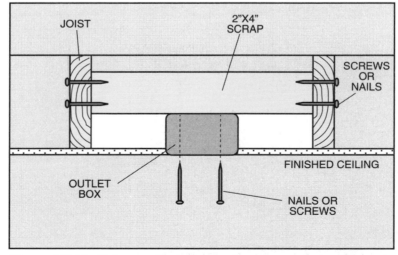

Figure 4-D-11. *Make sure the bottom surface does not extend beyond the finished surface of the wall or ceiling.*

Boxes Designed for Heavy Loads

The NEC® has special requirements for installing heavy items such as ceiling fans and large lighting fixtures. It states that outlet boxes shall not be permitted as the sole means of support for ceiling fans. However, UL listed boxes designed for special applications and fan support are permitted as the sole means of support. Make sure you read the NEC® requirements covering ceiling fan support and the manufacturers directions before installation. Fan manufacturers and electrical device suppliers provide a variety of styles and designs of outlet boxes and support systems that meet or surpass NEC® requirements.

Boxes rated for ceiling fan and heavy load installations are available in both nonmetallic and metallic types. **Figure 4-D-12** illustrates two type of nonmetallic boxes rated for heavy loads. They are installed to the ceiling joists by special brackets and screws according to the manufacturer's installation requirements.

Figure 4-D-13 illustrates two type of metallic boxes. The box system at the left consists of a UL rated box and metal support bar which is installed between the ceiling joists. The box at the right is attached directly to the ceiling framework with a special bracket.

Author's Note:
Special UL rated boxes are required for ceiling fan and heavy fixture installations.

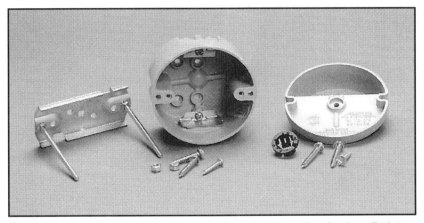

Figure 4-D-12. *Types of nonmetallic boxes rated for ceiling fan installations.*

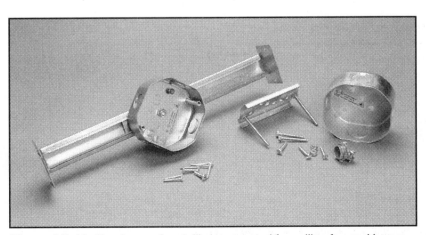

Figure 4-D-13. *Two types of metallic boxes rated for ceiling fan and heavy load installations.*

■ Mounting Fans & Heavy Fixtures

Mounting ceiling fans and heavy fixtures require special hanger assemblies or special outlet boxes rated for this type of installation. A variety of ceiling fan boxes and support systems are available commercially for installing most fan sizes and weights.

Two methods of ceiling fan installations are illustrated below. **Figure 4-D-14** illustrates a simple installation using an outlet box rated for fan installations. It is installed directly to the ceiling joist or other framing member using 1-1/2 to 2-inch wood screws Figure 4-D-15 illustrates one of many different types of hanger assemblies rated for ceiling fan installation. Each support method or system must be installed using listed materials and equipment rated for the fan or fixture weight it will be support. And each much be securely fastened to framework of the ceiling. Make sure you carefully read the manufacturer's installation directions for each fan style and type before beginning the installation process.

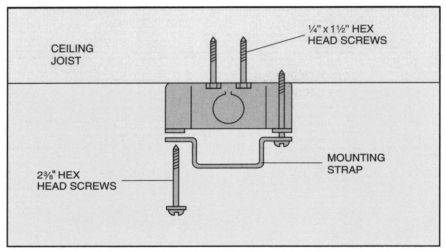

Figure 4-D-14. *A metal box typical of the type rated for ceiling fan and heavy fixture installation.*

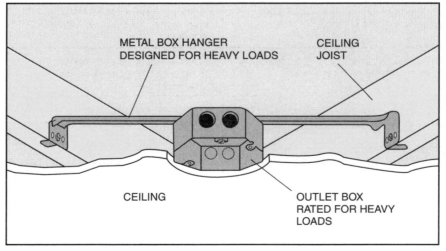

Figure 4-D-15. *A ceiling fan assembly kit typical of the types available for ceiling fan installations.*

E. Electrical Box Size Requirements

The NEC® requires that all outlet, device and junction boxes must be large enough to provide free space for all enclosed conductors, equipment, fittings and other supports. This is to assure that all components inside the box will have sufficient air circulation to keep them cool and free from overheating.

NEC® Table 370-16 (a) gives standard metal boxes and their dimensions in cubic inches and the maximum number of conductors that may be installed in each box size. **NEC® Table 370-16 (b)** gives the volume of space required per conductor for each size of conductor. Conductor sizes in both tables range from No. 18 AWG to No. 6 AWG. Tables 370-16 a& b are calculated for metallic boxes while Table 370-16 b is used for calculating nonmetallic boxes sizes.

Because most electrical installations require a combination of switches, receptacles, mounting devices, studs or cable clamps that require space within the box, you will be required to calculate the volume of each of these items and arrive at a cumulative total (cubic inches) to determine the total volume fill permitted for each size box. Determining the total volume fill for a box is based on <u>5</u> factors identified by the NEC®. These factors are shown in **Table 4-1** below.

Table 4-1		
Box Fill Calculation Factors		
(Based on cubic inch volume)		
Types	**Conditions**	**Volume Allowance Factor**
Conductor Fill	Each conductor that originates outside the box and is spliced or terminates within the box. Each conductor that passes through the box without splices or termination.	Volume of **(1)** for each conductor within box See NEC Table 370-16 (10 for conductor volume in cubic inches
Internal Clamp Fill	One or more cable clamps present within the box	Volume of **(1)** for one or more clamps within box based on largest conductor size
Support Fittings Fill	One or more fixture studs or hickeys present within the box	Volume of **(1)** for each fitting type within box based on largest conductor size.
Device & Equipment Fill	For each yoke or strap that contains one or more devices or equipment.	Volume of **(2)** for each yoke or strap within box based on largest conductor size.
Equipment Grounding Conductor Fill	One or more equipment grounding conductors present within the box	Volume of **(1)** for largest equipment grounding conductor size in box

Figures **4-E-1** and **4-E-2** are examples of typical wiring installations that will likely require you to determine the cubic inch volume of a box using the volume factors shown in **Table 4-E-1**, **NEC® Tables 370-16 (a)** and **370-16 (b)**. By using the examples illustrated and the appropriate NEC® tables, you will be able to calculate the volume of any device, outlet or junction box with ease.

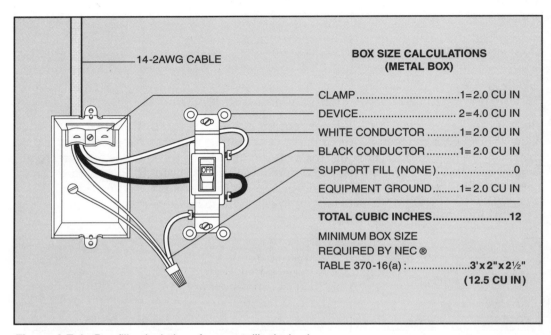

Figure 4-E-1. *Box fill calculations for a metallic device box.*

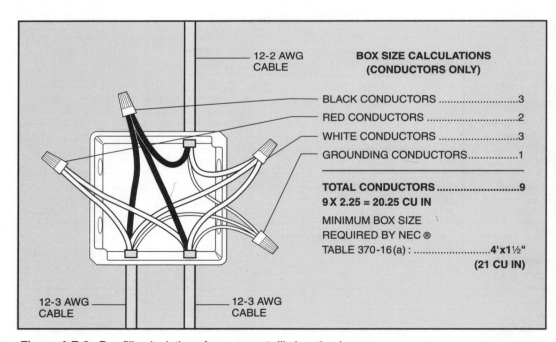

Figure 4-E-2. *Box fill calculations for a nonmetallic junction box.*

Cables & Conductors

"Wiring" is the term universally used to describe the process of installing a wiring system. While the term adequately covers the general process of electrical installation, it is important that you become familiar with the correct terminology for electrical equipment, devices and materials. The **wire** used for installing the wiring system, is technically called a **cable.** It is more accurately called a **conductor.** Both terms may be used correctly and interchangeably, however, there are distinct differences.

A **cable** may be described as a factory assembly of two or more conductors having an overall covering. This covering, or **sheath**, may be made of plastic, pvc, vinyl, rubber or metal. Its purpose is to protect the conductors from damage and hold them together as a single unit. A factory assembled cable, such as the one shown in **Figure 5-1** below, will also contain markings on the outer covering **(sheath)** indicating the size and number of insulated conductors *(grounding conductors are indicated but not counted)*, cable type and voltage rating. This information is required on all electrical cables.

In this chapter, you will learn about the types of cables and conductors commonly used in residential wiring systems. These are discussed under the topics:

A. Electrical Conductors

B. Cable Types

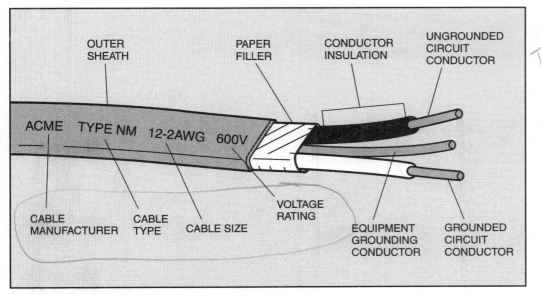

Figure 5-1. *Parts of a typical electrical cable.*

A. Electrical Conductors

A **conductor** is the term used to describe the individual wires bundled inside a cable sheath. Conductors carry—or conduct—the electrical current within the circuit. The number of conductors in the cable may vary depending on the circuit requirements. Conductors commonly used in most residential wiring practices are generally made from two types of materials, copper and aluminum, or a combination of the two materials: **(Figure 5-A-1)**.

Copper is considered the best material for cable conductors because of its exceptional ability to conduct electricity, its durability and because it has proven to give few problems over long periods of use **(Figure 5-A-1a)**.

Aluminum is often used where larger conductor sizes are necessary, such as in service entrances and feeder circuits. Aluminum, because it does not conduct electrical current as well as copper, must also be sized larger than copper to carry the same electrical load. Generally, aluminum conductors must be rated one trade size larger than copper conductors to safely carry the equivalent load **(Figure 5A-1b)**. In an installation requiring a No. 8 AWG copper conductor, its equivalent in aluminum would require a larger, No. 6 AWG conductor.

Copper-clad aluminum wire may also be permitted for use with certain exceptions. It is comprised of aluminum wire core with an outer copper coating **(Figure 5-A-1c)**. It may be used only with approved, UL listed wiring devices rated for its use. Some devices are rated for solid copper conductors only while others may be rated for either solid copper or copper-clad aluminum conductors. You should always check the device rating before installing conductors.

*NEC® Reference
For more on conductors and their properties, see NEC® Article 336*

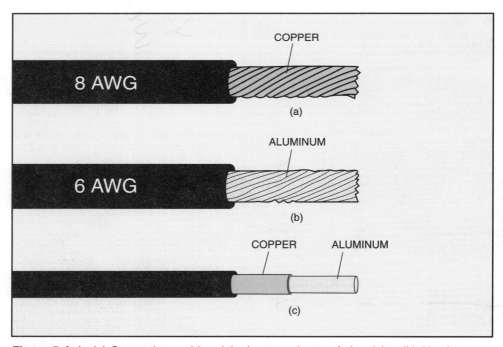

Figure 5-A-1. *(a) Copper is considered the best conductor of electricity. (b) Aluminum may be used where larger conductors are required. (c) Copper -clad aluminum may only be used with devices rated for its use.*

Conductor size is measured using the **American Wire Gauge (AWG)** rating system. With this system, the smaller the number rating, the larger the conductor size; the larger the number rating, the smaller the conductor size **(Figure 5-A-2)**.

For example: A No. 8 AWG conductor has a larger diameter than a No. 10 AWG conductor— but is smaller than a No. 6 AWG conductor. When in doubt about the size of a conductor, always check to make sure the correct size is being used before attempting an installation. A good method for determining the diameter of a conductor is to use the openings found on the combination wiring tool **(Figure 5-A-3)** or a wire stripper **(Figure 5-A-4)**.

Another method used for determining the size of a conductor is by its **kcmil** rating. **Kcmil equals one thousand circular mils.** One **circular mil** is the area of a circle with a diameter of 1/1000-inch and is used to describe the cross sectional area of an electrical conductor. It is commonly used to determine the true diameter for stranded and solid copper and aluminum conductors. It is also used when identifying conductor sizes larger than 4/0 AWG.

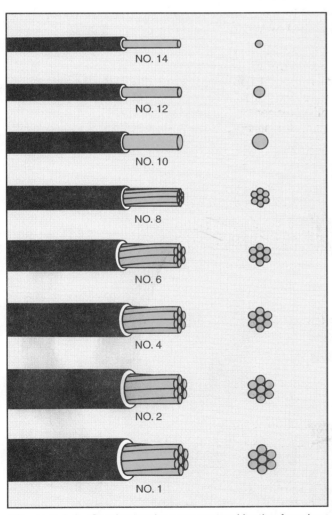

Figure 5-A-2. *Conductor sizes are gauged by the American Wire Gauge rating system. The smaller the AWG number, the larger the wire size. The larger the AWG number, the smaller the wire size.*

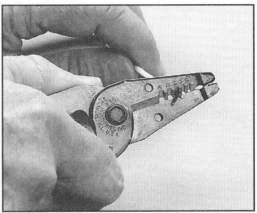

Figure 5-A-3. *A combination wiring tool can be used to measure conductor sizes.*

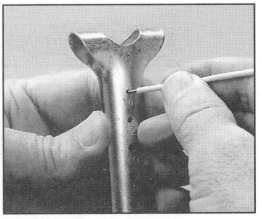

Figure 5-A-4. *A wire stripper can also be used for measuring conductor sizes.*

The ability of a conductor to carry current at a specific capacity is called **ampacity**. The ampacity of a conductor is measured in **amperes**. The NEC® defines ampacity as *"the current in amperes a conductor can carry continuously under conditions of use without exceeding its temperature rating."* As you might expect, the larger the conductor, the greater its ability to carry current — and usually, the greater its cost. Therefore, it is part of the electrician's job to select the proper size cable/conductors, of the correct ampacity, for each circuit. **(Figure 5-A-5)** shows the most common sizes of conductors used in residential wiring and its ampacity rating at both 60°C (celcius /centigrade) and 75°C temperatures.

NEC® References
For more on electrical conductors, see NEC® Articles
110-14
310-13
310-16

- **General Purpose Circuits** usually require **No. 12** or **No. 14 AWG** conductors with **15-20 ampere** overload protection.

- **Small Appliance Circuits,** because the load they are required to carry is larger than general purpose circuits, these circuits require **No. 12 AWG conductors with 20-ampere** overload protection.

- **Individual Equipment Circuits.** which carry even larger load requirements than both general purpose or small appliance circuits, require **No. 10 AWG** or **larger conductors with 30-ampere** or larger overload protection.

Author's Note:
The NEC® permits the use of #14 AWG conductors with 15-ampere overcurrent protection. However, local codes may prohibit its use for branch circuits.

AWG (SIZE)	AMPERAGE RATING @ 60° C	AMPERAGE RATING @ 75° C
	101 AMPERES OR LESS	101 AMPERES OR MORE
#1	110	130
#2	95	115
#4	70	85
#6	55	65
#8	40	50
#10	30	35
#12	20	25
#14	15	20

Figure 5-A-5. Common conductor sizes and amperage ratings used for most residential wiring installations.

Conductors commonly used in residential wiring, like the cable itself, are also protected by an NEC® approved insulated covering — usually plastic, pvc or vinyl. The type of outer covering and the type and number of conductors determine how and where the cable will be used. Letters, or combinations of letters called **cable nomenclature,** identifies the application and conductor insulation covering which is required on all electrical cable. **Table 5-1** illustrates some of this cable nomenclature. **Table 5-2** illustrates some of the common types of insulation designations and their applications. For a complete listing see, **NEC® Table 310-13.**

Table 5-1
Examples of Cable Nomenclature

T	Thermoplastic. Rated for 60° Celsius (centigrade) temperatures.
X	Thermoset cross-linked polyethylene insulation.
R	Thermoset rubber insulation.
W	Moisture resistant.
H	Heat resistant. Adds 15° to the 60° Celsius conductor operating temperature.
HH	High heat resistance. Adds 30° to the 60° Celsius conductor operating temperature.
HHW	Maximum operating temperatures of 75° Celsius in wet locations and 90° Celsius in dry locations.
F	Fixture Wire
FF	Flexible Fixture Wire
N	Nylon overall outer jacket.

Table 5-2
Single Conductor Insulation Designations

Conductor Markings	Insulation Type	Permitted Uses	Operating Temps	Conductor AWG Range	Outer Jacket
TW	Thermoplastic (PVC)	Wet Locations	60°C	14 AWG thru 1000 kcmil	yes
THW	Thermoplastic (PVC)	Wet Locations	75°C	14 AWG thru 1000 kcmil	no
THWN	Thermoplastic (PVC)	Wet Locations	High Heat 75°C	14 AWG thru 1000 kcmil	yes nylon
THHN	Thermoplastic (PVC)	Wet Locations	High Heat 75°C	14 AWG thru 1000 kcmil	yes nylon

Table 5-3 shows the basic circuit types and the recommended conductor size and overcurrent protection ratings for general purpose, small appliance and individual branch circuits.

Table 5-3 Recommended Conductor Sizes and Overcurrent Protection For Residential Branch Circuits		
Circuit Type	**Conductor Size**	**Maximum Overcurrent Protection (Amperes)**
General Purpose	14/12	15/20
Small Appliance	12	20
Individual	10 or larger	30 or larger

Table 5-4 shows some typical individual circuit appliances and equipment and their recommended AWG conductor and overcurrent protection ratings.

Table 5-4 Recommended Conductor Sizes and Overcurrent Protection For Individual Branch Circuits		
Circuit Type	**AWG Conductor Size (Copper)**	**Maximum Overcurrent Protection (Amperes)**
Air Conditioner	12	20
Water Heater	12/10	20/30
Separate Oven	10	30
Counter Top	10	30
Self Contained Range	6	50
Clothes Dryer	10	30
Central Heating/Air	8/6	40/60
Electric Furnace	6	50
Water Pump	12	20

The ampacity of a conductor is determined by the rating of the device (switch receptacle, appliance or equipment) to which it is connected. **Table 5-5** below shows examples of some of these rating.

A complete listing of insulated conductors and their ampacity ratings can be found in **NEC® Table 310-16.** As an exercise in using a table to find the allowable ampere rating for conductors, find the values shown below in the following examples:

- A #8 AWG, TW rated conductor has an allowable ampacity of 40 amperes @ 60°C termination.

- A #8 AWG, THW rated conductor has an allowable capacity of 50 amperes @ 75°C termination.

- A #8 AWG, THHW conductor has an allowable capacity of 55 amperes @ 90°C termination.

Author's Note: NM conductors have an insulation factor rating of 90° C. However, NM conductor insulation is limited to a 60°C rating.

Table 5-5 Temperatures and Amperage Ratings for Common Sizes of Insulated Copper and Aluminum Conductors							
Insulated Copper				Insulated Aluminum			
	Temperature Ratings				Temperature		
AWG Size	60° C (140° F)	75° C (167° F)	90° C (194° F)	AWG Size	60° C (140° F)	75° C (167° F)	90° C (194° F)
	Amperage Rating				Amperage Rating		
14	20	20	25	14	–	–	–
12	25	25	30	12	20	20	25
10	30	35	40	10	25	30	35
8	40	50	55	8	30	40	45
6	55	65	75	6	40	50	60
4	70	85	95	4	55	65	75
2	95	115	130	2	75	90	100
1	110	130	150	1	85	100	115

Conductors and the functions they perform can be identified not only by their amperage markings and AWG size or kcmil rating, but also by the color coding of their insulation. The NEC® requires that each conductor in a cable be color coded to indicate the function it is to perform in the circuit. **Figure 5-A-7** shows the color coding scheme and function for conductors commonly used in most residential wiring.

- **Black** - Ungrounded conductor; carries current to the load at full voltage.

- **White** - Grounded circuit conductor; returns current from the load to its source at zero (0) voltage. In certain uses may also be a neutral conductor.

- **Bare** - Equipment grounding conductor

- **Green** - Insulated equipment grounding conductor

- **Red** - Ungrounded conductor; carries current at full voltage in three conductor cables.

NEC® References
For more on conductor uses, see NEC® Articles
200-7
310-12

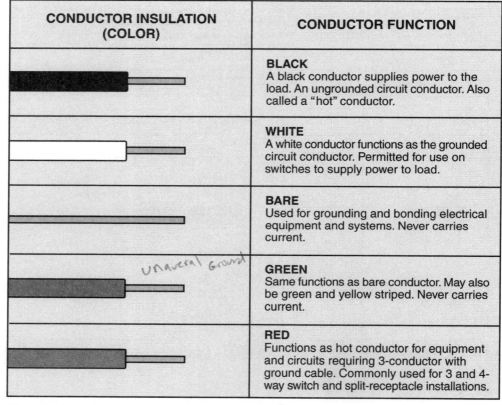

CONDUCTOR INSULATION (COLOR)	CONDUCTOR FUNCTION
BLACK	**BLACK** A black conductor supplies power to the load. An ungrounded circuit conductor. Also called a "hot" conductor.
WHITE	**WHITE** A white conductor functions as the grounded circuit conductor. Permitted for use on switches to supply power to load.
BARE	**BARE** Used for grounding and bonding electrical equipment and systems. Never carries current.
GREEN	**GREEN** Same functions as bare conductor. May also be green and yellow striped. Never carries current.
RED	**RED** Functions as hot conductor for equipment and circuits requiring 3-conductor with ground cable. Commonly used for 3 and 4-way switch and split-receptacle installations.

Figure 5-A-6. *The NEC® requires that conductor insulation be color coded.*

B. Cable Types

There are several different types of electrical cable available for almost every type of wiring installation. Each is required to contain markings that help the electrician identify its type and use (**Figure 5-B-1**). These markings must appear on the cable's outer sheath at 24-inch intervals show the following information:

- **Cable type**
- Maximum working **voltage**
- Manufacturer's **name, trademark** or other identifying markings.
- **Size: AWG (American Wire Gauge)**/or **kcmil** rating.

The two types of cable typically used in residential wiring are:

1. **NM (Nonmetallic) - NM** cable is used for most general purpose, small appliance and individual electrical circuits in the typical residence. It is available as two-conductor with ground and three-conductor with ground. The grounding conductor may be bare or insulated in each type (**Figure-5-B-2**).

2. **SE (Service Entrance) -** Service entrance cable is used to supply the power from theservice drop connections at the weather head, to the meter and on to the service entrance panel. It must contains two insulated conductors and one uninsulated conductor (**Figure 5-B-3**).

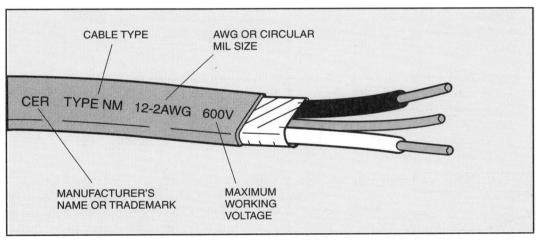

Figure 5-B-1. Electrical cable is required to show the cable type, voltage, name, AWG size or kcmil rating and manufacturer's trademark.

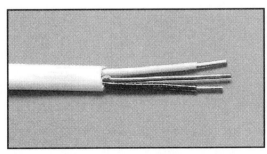

Figure 5-B-2. An example of NM cable typically used in wiring residential branch circuits.

Figure 5-B-3. An example of service entrance cable used to supply power to the SEP.

■ Nonmetallic Sheathed Cable (NM)

Nonmetallic sheathed cable is commonly used for most residential wiring installations. It is available with two or three insulated conductors and a grounding conductor which may, or may not be insulated. **Figure 5-B-4** illustrates examples of some typical NM cable /conductors commonly used in residential electrical installations.

NEC® References
For more on NM,
NMC and NMS
cable, see NEC®
Articles
215-5
310-10
336

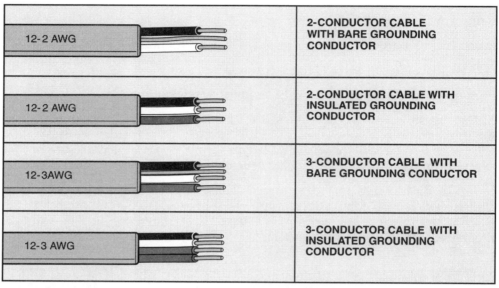

12-2 AWG	**2-CONDUCTOR CABLE WITH BARE GROUNDING CONDUCTOR**
12-2 AWG	**2-CONDUCTOR CABLE WITH INSULATED GROUNDING CONDUCTOR**
12-3AWG	**3-CONDUCTOR CABLE WITH BARE GROUNDING CONDUCTOR**
12-3 AWG	**3-CONDUCTOR CABLE WITH INSULATED GROUNDING CONDUCTOR**

Figure 5-B-4. *Types of NM cable commonly used for residential wiring.*

Author's Note:
Type NM cable is
not permitted
for use where it
will be exposed
to sunlight.

1. **Type NM cable** is most often used for residential wiring installations. It may be installed for both exposed and concealed work in normally dry locations. This includes air voids in masonry block or tile walls where excessive moisture is not present. Type NM cable **may not** be installed where it is exposed to corrosive fumes or vapors, nor can it be imbedded in masonry, concrete or plaster.

2. **Type NMC cable** meets the requirements for NM cable and is also fungus and corrosion resistant. It is commonly used in both exposed and concealed work in dry, moist, damp, or corrosive locations. Once popular, it is seldom produced today. UF cable meets the same requirements for installation and is normally used in place of NMC type cable.

3. **Type NMS cable** may be used for both exposed and concealed work in normally dry locations. It can also be used in masonry block or tile walls where they are not exposed or not subject to excessive moisture or dampness.

These cable types are permitted for use in one and two-family dwelling construction, multi-family dwelling—and other structures with certain exceptions. These exceptions and more information on where cables may be installed can be found in **NEC® Article 336**. Each is manufactured in copper, in sizes No. 14 AWG through No. 2 AWG and in aluminum in sizes No. 12 AWG through No. 2 AWG.

■ Service Entrance and Feeder Cables

Service entrance cables supply the electrical power from entrance head to the meter and on to the SEP. **Feeder cables** supply electrical power from the SEP to the subpanel. They may be constructed with single conductors or multiple conductors in copper or aluminum and are covered with a protective covering. Because of their larger size requirements and expense, most residential installations use aluminum conductors rather than the more expensive copper conductors .

Figure 5-B-5 illustrates four types of cable recommended by the NEC® for service entrance and feeder cable installations.

1. **Type SE Cable - (Figure 5-B-5a) -** cable type used for service entrance installations. Contains three conductors with a flame retardant, moisture resistant covering.

2. **Type USE Cable - (Figure 5-B-5b) -** a three-conductor cable used for underground service installations. It has a moisture-resistant covering, but is not flame - retardant. It may also be used for underground feeder circuits and outdoor branch circuits.

3. **Type UF Cable - (Figure 5-B-5c) -** can be used for direct burial of underground feeder circuits. It cannot be buried in concrete. It is also approved for use in interior installations where wet, dry or corrosive conditions are likely to exist.

4. **Type SER Cable - (Figure 5-B-5d) -** a four-conductor cable assembled in a round configuration. It is commonly used where four conductors are required for feeder cable installations.

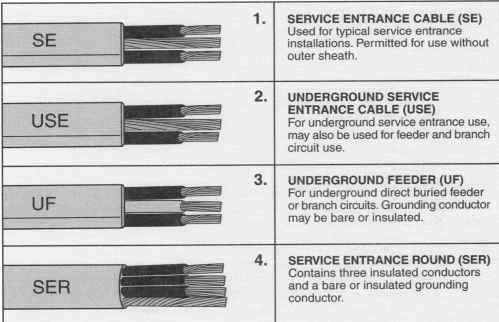

SE	**1.**	**SERVICE ENTRANCE CABLE (SE)** Used for typical service entrance installations. Permitted for use without outer sheath.
USE	**2.**	**UNDERGROUND SERVICE ENTRANCE CABLE (USE)** For underground service entrance use, may also be used for feeder and branch circuit use.
UF	**3.**	**UNDERGROUND FEEDER (UF)** For underground direct buried feeder or branch circuits. Grounding conductor may be bare or insulated.
SER	**4.**	**SERVICE ENTRANCE ROUND (SER)** Contains three insulated conductors and a bare or insulated grounding conductor.

*NEC® References
For more on service entrance cables, see NEC® Articles
336
338
339*

Figure 5-B-5. *Types of service entrance cable used for residential wiring.*

Notes

Installing Circuit Cables & Conductors

6

Now that you've been introduced the basic types of cables and conductors used for residential wiring, it's time to learn how to properly install them at the rough-in stage of construction **(Figure 6-1)**.

To install a circuit, You must first be able to plan the circuit route through the framework that will carry the electrical cable from the SEP or subpanel to the outlets along the circuit run. It must be planned and installed to function economically, efficiently and safely. And it must be planned and installed to be protected from damage long after the installation has been completed.

In this chapter you will learn how to connect circuit cables and conductors. These procedures are discussed under the following headings:

A. Installing Cable

B. Unrolling Electrical Cable

C. Starting the Circuit Run

D. Securing Cable to the Framework

E. Securing Cable to Device and Outlet Boxes

F. Splicing Conductors

Figure 6-1. *Circuits in new construction are installed during the rough-in stage of construction.*

A. Installing Cable

"**Pulling**" is a term commonly used to describe the process for running electrical cables in the framework to its point of installation at the outlet box. **(Figure 6-A-1).** In order to create a branch circuit, cable must be routed through and along the studs, rafters, and floor and ceiling joists of the building framework. Before you begin the task of pulling cable through a circuit route, it is important that you become familiar with the various options, techniques and procedures typically used for installing electrical cable.

Whether electrical circuits are to be routed through studs, floor joists, ceiling joists, rafters or a combination of all, you can assure that the job will be easier, neater, safer and will meet the NEC® requirements by learning and reviewing these simple suggestions.

▲ Visually line up the planned circuit route.

▲ Drill the holes in the center of each stud or joist.

▲ Keep the holes in line as closely as possible. Your work will not only look neater, but it will also make it easier to install the cable. Holes that are not aligned will make it harder to pull the cable from one stud or joist to the other.

▲ After cable has been pulled to all outlet boxes along the circuit run, check your work.

● Make sure that the cable is free from severe kinks, cuts in the sheathing and has been installed without sharp bends. The NEC® requires that no cable bend shall have a radius less than five (5) times the wide diameter of cable.

● Make sure that you have allowed enough cable in each outlet box to make the necessary device connections.

NEC® References
For more on cable
installation, see
NEC® Articles
300
330-8

FIGURE 6-A-1. *Cable is pulled (routed) through holes drilled in the framework to the outlets in the circuit and terminates in the service panel (lower right).*

■ Drilling Holes in the Framework

In traditional wood frame construction, electrical circuit cables are routed through wooden studs, floor and ceiling joists and rafters.

This is commonly done by drilling holes through the framing members. Having the right equipment and knowing why and how to do the job makes the work go faster and easier. A simple way to accomplish this is by using a power drill **(Figure 6-A-2)** and the proper type and size of drill bit. Holes for most types of nonmetallic cable used in electrical installations range from a minimum of 5/8-inch to a maximum of 1-inch in diameter **(Figure 6-A-3)**. Bits may be flat or round depending on availability and preference. Larger diameter holes may require more specialized types of equipment.

Holes should be drilled at the approximate center of the framing member. This is because holes drilled in the center of the stud are at a neutral axis and do not weaken the framing member. The hole must not be less than 1-1/4 inches from the edge of a standard 2"X4" wood stud **(Figure 6-A-4)**. If less than 1-1/4 inches, the cable must be protected from nails by a bushing or a steel plate at least 1/16 inch thick **(Figure 6-A-5)**. These can be found at your local electrical supplier or home center electrical department.

NEC® Reference
For more on installing cable , see NEC® Article 300-4

Author's Note:
Never make holes in framework larger than necessary. Holes that are too large weaken the structure.

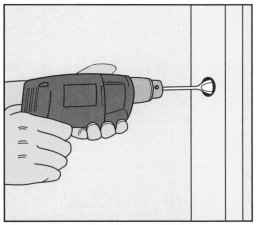

Figure 6-A-2. *Power drills are commonly used for drilling holes in wood framing.*

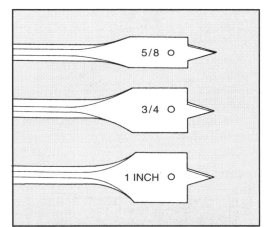

Figure 6-A-3. *Drill bit sizes used for drilling holes for residential wiring.*

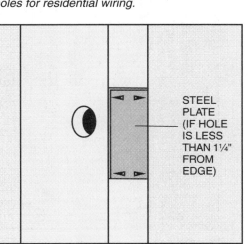
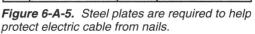

Figure 6-A-4. *Always drill holes in the center of framing stud.*

Figure 6-A-5. *Steel plates are required to help protect electric cable from nails.*

■ Installing Cable in Studwalls

After selecting the path the electrical circuit will take, you can now begin to drill holes in the studs and joists for pulling the cable. Below are four methods commonly used by electricians for drilling holes in studs for easy cable installation:

NEC® References
For more on cable
protection and
support, see
NEC® Articles
333-12
336-6 b&c

▲ Holes Drilled Parallel to Floor

You may run the cable parallel to the floor making gradual turns for changes in direction and elevation **(Figure 6-A-6)**.

▲ Gradual Changes in Elevation

Holes may be drilled in a path that will allow for gradual changes in elevation **(Figure 6-A-7)**.

▲ Holes Drilled at Bottom of Studwall

With an increased emphasis on improving the efficiency of stud wall insulation, builders have begun routing electrical cable through holes drilled near the bottom of the stud near the sole plate **(Figure 6-A-8)**. This allows batt or roll insulation to be placed between the studs without interference from the circuit cable.

▲ Notches in Studs

Author's Note:
Although permitted
by the NEC®, local
codes may not
permit notching
studs for cable
installation.

With this method, notches cut into the studs must be covered with steel plates **(Figure 6-A-9)**. The NEC® requires that a steel plate, at least 1/16-inch thick, be installed over the notch to protect the cable. Although approved by the NEC®, many local codes do not allow this type of installation. Check with your local building inspection office before using this type of installation.

(Left) Figure 6-A-6.
Holes drilled parallel
to the floor.

(Right) Figure 6-A-7.
Holes drilled to permit
for a gradual change
in elevation.

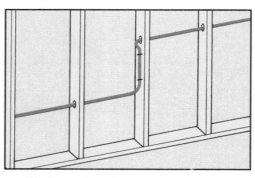

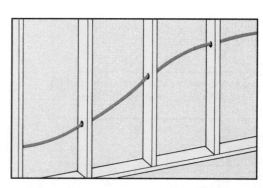

(Left) Figure 6-A-8.
Holes drilled near
bottom of studwall.

(Right) Figure 6-A-9.
Notches cut in studs
are not always
approved by local
codes.

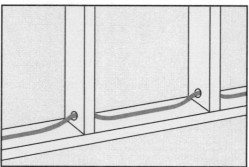

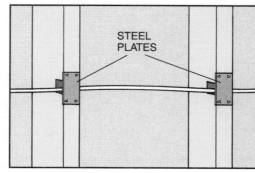

STEEL
PLATES

■ Installing Cable in Ceiling & Floor Joists

Routing electrical cables through ceiling and floor joists each requires a slightly different method from that used in routing cable through wall studs.

▲ Holes Drilled in Joists

This method is used most often in unfinished attic and basement areas where cable sizes are No. 8 AWG or smaller **(Figure 6-A-10)**.

▲ Routed Over Joists

Routing cables over ceiling joists is accomplished by simply drilling a hole through the top plate and pulling the cable over the joists to continue its route **(Figure 6-A-11)**.

▲ Guard Strips

This method is often used in unfloored attic areas. The cable is protected by boards equal in thickness to that of the cable and installed within 6 ft. from the attic entrance **(Figure 6-A-12)**. Cables installed parallel to the ceiling and floor joists or rafters must be installed with their nearest outside surface not less than 1-1/4 inches from the nearest edge of the framing member.

▲ Running Boards

Circuit cables No. 8 AWG or larger, must be attached to **running boards.** Running boards consist **of** 1"X 4" wooden boards nailed end-to-end that run the full length of the cable run. **(Figure 6-A-13)**. No. 6 AWG or smaller cables must be attached directly to the lower edge of the joists or in holes drilled through the joists.

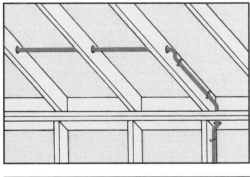

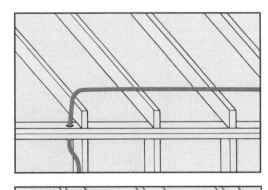

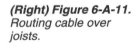

(Left) Figure 6-A-10.
Routing cable through holes drilled in joists.

(Right) Figure 6-A-11.
Routing cable over joists.

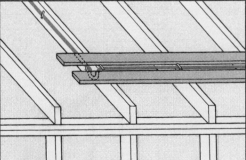

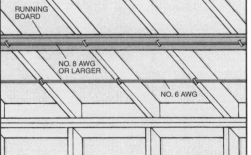

(Left) Figure 6-A-12.
Routing cable using guard strips.

(Right) Figure 6-A-13.
Routing cable on running boards.

■ Installing Cable in Metal Frame Construction

Installing electrical cable in a metal frame building requires special considerations for installing cable and device boxes to the framing members. **The American Iron and Steel Institute** recommends the following steps and materials for installing NM cable in metal frame construction **(Figure 6-A-14)**. These materials are readily available from electrical suppliers and home improvement centers

- **Snap-in grommets** or **insulators** made of plastic or vinyl are required to protect the cable sheathing from the sharp edges of the steel studs.

- Electrical device boxes with side mounting brackets are recommended because they are easily mounted to the sides of the metal studs using 3/4-inch, **#6 sharp-point** or **self-drilling screws**. Device and outlet boxes may be either nonmetallic or metallic For studs thicker than 18-27 mils, **#8 self drilling screws** are recommended.

- To secure NM electrical cable to metal studs, (two) 1/4- inch holes are drilled into the stud at the NEC ® recommended distance above or below the outlet box. A **plastic zip-tie** can be used to attach the cable by routing it through the holes and tightening it securely.

Author's Note: Always check local building codes before installing cable in metal frame construction.

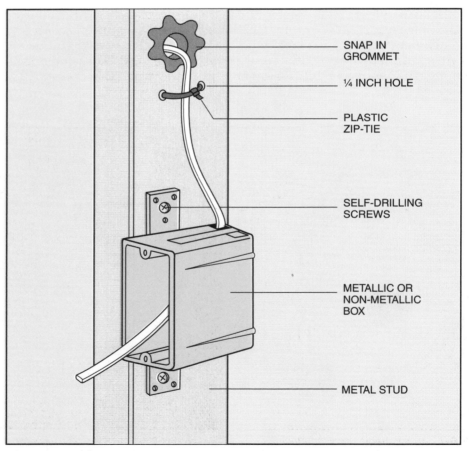

SNAP IN GROMMET

¼ INCH HOLE

PLASTIC ZIP-TIE

SELF-DRILLING SCREWS

METALLIC OR NON-METALLIC BOX

METAL STUD

Figure 6-A-14. *Installing cable in metal frame construction.*

B. Unrolling Electrical Cable

Nonmetallic sheathed cable used in residential electrical installations is usually purchased from the electrical supplier as a roll packaged in plastic, cardboard box or on a reel. It can be purchased in pre-packaged lengths from 25 ft. to 250 ft. or more. Larger amounts of cable are usually purchased on reels. Smaller amounts — 25 ft. or less — can be purchased in varying lengths from the electrical supplier.

It is important that you learn the correct procedure for unrolling electrical cable from a box, roll or reel. This simple procedure can become a frustrating task if not started properly.

Prepackaged Cable

When unrolling electrical cable from a box or roll, it is best to begin from the inside of the coil **(Figure 6-B-1)**. Some cable manufacturers often provide a circular cut-out or some other type of directions on the cable box indicating the starting point for unrolling the cable. Failure to follow these directions can lead to cable kinks and frustration.

Reel Cable

Cable is also available on reels. Reels are usually desirable when large amounts of cable are needed for a job. Unrolling cable from a reel can be simplified by using a reel holder such as the one shown in **Figure 6-B-2**. Commercial reel holders are available from your electrical supply house, or you can construct your own using only scrap lumber, a few nails or screws and a few simple hand tools.

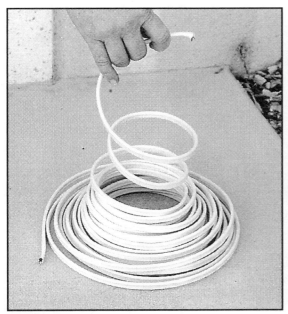

Figure 6-B-1. *Always begin unrolling electrical cable from inside the coil.*

Figure 6-B-2. *A commercial reel holder.*

C. Starting the Circuit Run

It is good practice to think of a circuit run as beginning at the SEP or subpanel. It can be said that all branch circuits either begin—or end— at either of these two locations. Once you gain more knowledge and become more proficient at installation procedures, you may wish to start the circuit installation some other point along the route. But for now, let's begin at the service entrance panel.

Author's Note:
Make sure to always install enough cable into the SEP cabinet for making branch circuit connctions to any point in the panel box.

• Start by placing one end of the circuit cable through one of the knockouts in the cabinet **(Figure 6-C-1)**. Knockouts are located at the top, bottom and sides of the SEP cabinet. Pull enough cable into the cabinet to allow for the necessary connections that will be made when the circuit conductors are installed to their circuit breakers. Secure the cable to the cabinet using approved cable connectors.

• Identify each circuit cable after pulling it into the cabinet with the circuit number, type and location as it appears on the wiring plan. This will help eliminate possible confusion when you begin to install circuit cables to their circuit breakers later in the installation process. **Figure 6-C-2** illustrates how general purpose circuits #1, #2 and #3 on the sample wiring plan can be identified by writing the information on a piece of masking tape and wrapping it securely around the cable.

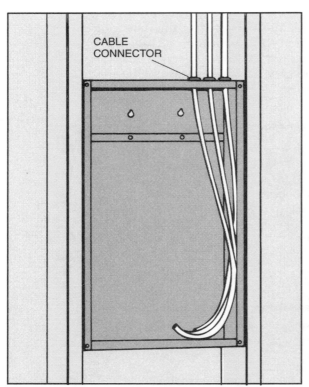

Figure 6-C-1. *Begin the circuit by placing the cable through the knock-outs in the SEP or subpanel cabinet.*

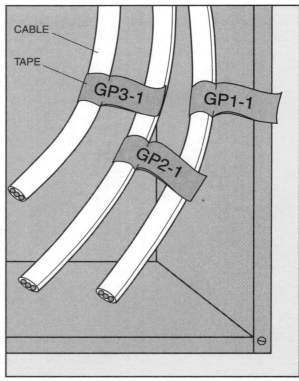

Figure 6-C-2. *Identify circuit cables in the panel board by label ing them.*

As shown earlier, circuits are commonly routed through and over ceiling and floor joists and through holes drilled in wall studs. Cable pulled into or from the service entrance panel may be routed through holes drilled in the top plate directly above the panel cabinet, through holes drilled in the studwalls enclosing the panel cabinet and through holes drilled in the bottom plate directly below the panel cabinet **(Figure 6-C-3)**.

One important consideration that must be made at this point of the installation is where and how the service entrance conductors are to reach and enter the service entrance panel cabinet. Service entrance conductors may enter at either the top or bottom of the cabinet

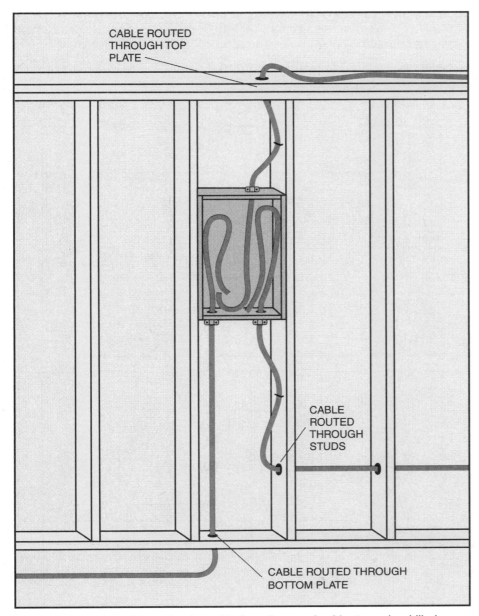

CABLE ROUTED THROUGH TOP PLATE

CABLE ROUTED THROUGH STUDS

CABLE ROUTED THROUGH BOTTOM PLATE

Figure 6-C-3. *Holes for routing the cable from the panel cabinet may be drilled through the top plate, wall studs or bottom plate.*

- Continue pulling the cable through holes drilled in the framing members until you reach the first outlet box in the circuit. Make sure that the cable makes gradual bends as it travels through the holes in framing members as it makes it way through the circuit run **(Figure 6-C-4a)**.

NEC® References
For more on installing conductors in device boxes, see NEC® Articles 300-14 336-16

- Pull the cable through one of the knockouts into the box. Allow a minimum of 6 to 8 inches of cable to remain in the box **(Figure 6-C-4b)**. This extra length of cable is necessary for making conductor connections to the device. One practice is to pull more cable into the box than the required 6 to 8 inches and after the cable sheathing has been stripped away, then cut the conductors to the proper length.

- To continue the circuit run, insert the second cable into another knockout in the device box **(Figure 6-C-4c)**. Make sure to leave enough cable exposed to make the required 6 to 8 inches finished length for device connections. Repeat this process until cable has been pulled to all outlet boxes on the circuit.

- Cut the cable to the desired length and fold back into the device box **(Figure 6-C-4d)**.

(Left) Figure 6-C-4a.
When pulling electrical cable through holes in the framing, make gradual bends.

(Right) Figure 6-C-4b.
Leave 6 to 8 inches of cable in the box.

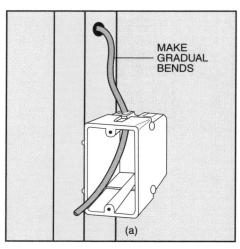
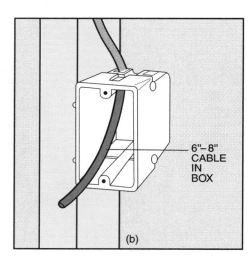

(Left) Figure 6-C-4c.
When continuing the circuit, insert a second cable into the device box.

(Right) Figure 6-C-4d.
Fold the cable into the box and out of the way.

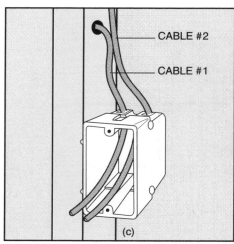
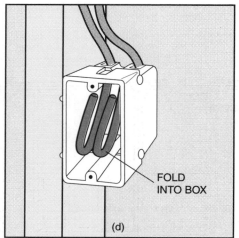

Some of the options commonly used when installing (pulling) cable to the device boxes in a circuit run are illustrated below in **Figures 6-C-5, 6-C-6** and **6-C-7**.

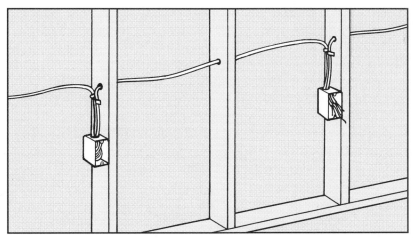

Figure 6-C-5. *Device boxes installed on the same side of a common wall.*

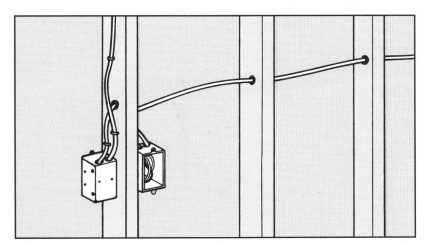

Figure 6-C-6. *Device boxes installed on opposite sides of the same stud.*

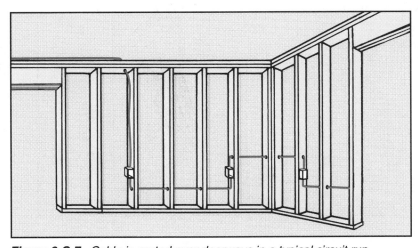

Figure 6-C-7. *Cable is routed over doorways in a typical circuit run.*

D. Securing Cable to the Framework

Now that the circuit cable has been run from the SEP to the outlet boxes in the circuit, you must secure the cable to the framework. The NEC® requires that electrical cable be secured by staples, cable straps or other approved fittings. These anchoring devices must be installed in a fashion that will protect the electrical cable during and after installation.

Electrical staples are commonly used for securing cable to the framework because of their ease of installation, popularity and low cost **(Figure 6-D-1)**. The staple must be installed properly so as not to damage the cable sheathing or the conductor insulation. Avoid bending or driving the staple too far into the cable.

Cable straps are also popular and do an excellent job of protecting the cable but are more expensive than staples **(Figure 6-D-2)**.

NEC® References
For more on securing cable and conductors, see NEC® Articles
336-15
336-18
370-17c

Author's Note:
Always take great care not to damage the cable when securing it with staples and straps.

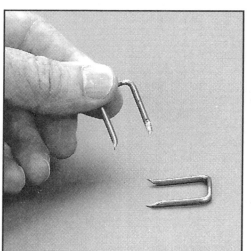
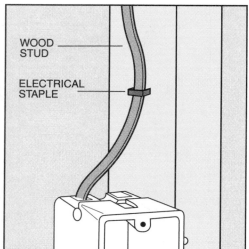

Figure 6-D-1. *Electrical staples are inexpensive and are commonly used for securing cable to the framework.*

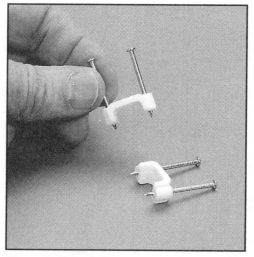
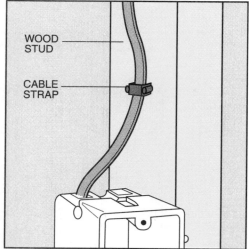

Figure 6-D-2. *Cable straps also offer additioal protection for the cable sheathing .*

The NEC® requires that circuit cable be attached to studs, joists, rafters and other framing members at the following intervals:

- When using **nonmetallic boxes,** cable must be secured to the framework within **8″** from its entry into the box **(Figure 6-D-3).**

- When using **metallic boxes,** cable must be secured to the framework within **12″** from its entry into the box **(Figure 6-D-4).**

- Cable running across or along studs, joists or rafters must be secured to the framework every **4-1/2 ft.** for the full length of the circuit run **(Figure 6-D-5).**

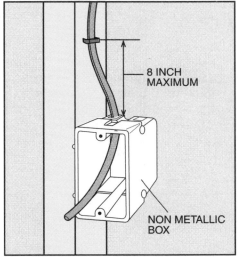

Figure 6-D-3. Cable must be secured within 8 inches of a nonmetallic box.

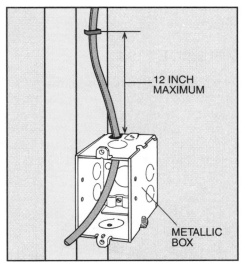

Figure 6-D-4. Cable must be secured within 12 inches of a metal box.

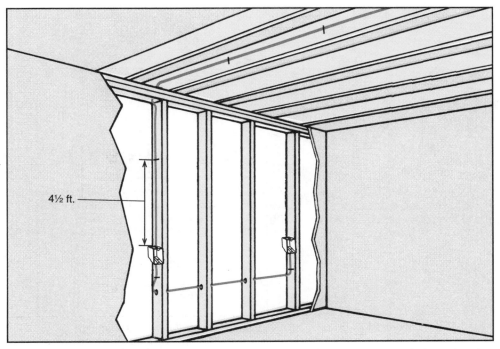

Figure 6-D-5. Electrical cable must be secured to the framework every 4-1/2 feet when it is run across joists, rafters and wall studs.

E. Securing Cable to Device & Outlet Boxes

With the conductors properly stripped to the correct exposure, secure the cable to the device or outlet box.

NEC® References For more on securing conductors in device boxes, see NEC® Article 370-17

■ Nonmetallic Boxes

If using nonmetallic device boxes for the circuit installation, the NEC® **does not require** that the cable be secured within the box **(Figure 6-E-1)**. However, the cable sheath must enter the box approximately **1/4-inch** before it is removed from the conductors. This provides extra protection for the cable conductors against cuts that may occur from the sharp edges of the knockouts.

■ Metallic Boxes

If using metallic device boxes, the NEC® **requires** that the cable be secured within the box by an approved cable clamp or cable connector. Just as with nonmetallic boxes, the cable with must enter the box with its protective sheathing intact for approximately **1/4 inch (Figure 6-E-2)**. This extra protection is particularly important in metal boxes that require the use of metal cable connectors and clamps.

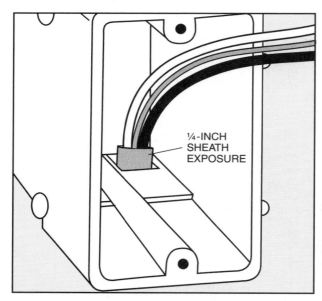

Figure 6-E-1. *Cable clamps and cable connectors are not required to secure cable in nonmetallic boxes. The cable protective sheathing should extend up to 1/4-inch inside the box.*

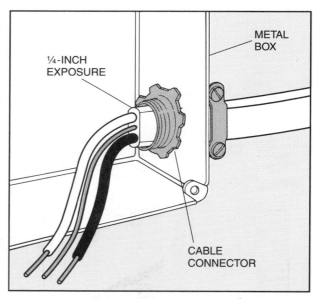

Figure 6-E-2. *Metallic boxes require the use of cable clamps or cable connectors for securing cable. The protective sheathing on the cable must extend approximately 1/4-inch beyond the cable connector.*

F. Splicing Conductors

The first step in preparing the cable for splicing is to remove the protective covering without damaging the conductors. A cable ripper is designed specifically for this function **(Figure 6-F-1)**. A knife can also be used but there is a danger of cutting too deeply into the cable and damaging the conductor insulation. Below are some simple steps illustrating how to remove the cable sheath.

- Place the cutting edge of the tool at a point on the cable you wish to start the cut and squeeze the cable ripper until the cutting point sinks into the cable sheath. Pull the cable ripper down the cable cutting through the sheathing. Repeat the process if necessary.

- Separate the outer sheath and the inner paper lining from the conductors and remove with side cutting pliers or a blunt-pointed knife **(Figure 6-F-2)**.

- Remove approximately **5/8" to 3/4"** of the insulation from the end of each conductor. This can be done using a wire stripper **(Figure 6-F-3) or** a bluntpointed knife blade **(Figure 6-F-4)**. Take care not damage the wire; a simple nick can weaken the conductor's ability to safely carry electricity.

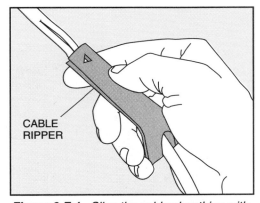

Figure 6-F-1. *Slice the cable sheathing with a cable ripper.*

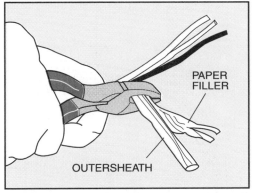

Figure 6-F-2. *Remove the outer sheathing and inner paper lining.*

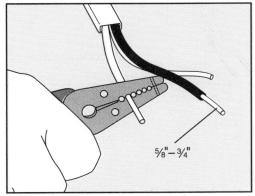

Figure 6-F-3. *Remove 5/8 to 3/4 inches of insulation from each conductor.*

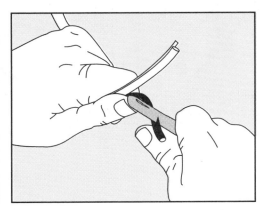

Figure 6-F-4. *Do not damage the conductor when removing the insulation.*

■ Solderless Connectors

The NEC® requires that cable/conductor splices (connections) conduct electrical current between two joined conductors with the same efficiency as solid, or unjoined conductors. Connections that are not joined together properly may permit **arcing.** This may cause a fire hazard or damage to equipment when the electrical system is placed in service.

Solderless connectors (Figure 6-F-5), by their definition, are connectors used to make conductor connections without the use of solder. Soldering was once the accepted method of splicing conductors but is seldom used in the modern wiring installations. Solderless connectors are easy to use, inexpensive and make quick, solid connections. They are also available at most hardware stores and electrical suppliers and come in a variety of styles, colors and sizes. Make sure that the materials you are using for splicing conductors are approved for the conditions under which they will be used and that all materials used are UL listed.

Solderless connectors used for most residential wiring applications are available in three basic types:

1. Wire Nuts

2. Crimped Connectors

3. Split-Bolt Connectors

Author's Note:
Use only listed materials when making conductor splices.

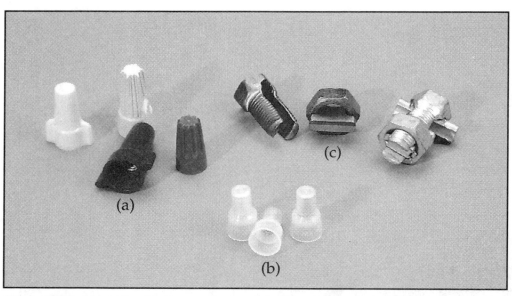

Figure 6-F-5. *Types of solderless connectors. (a) wire nuts. (b) crimped connectors. (c) split-bolt connectors.*

▲ Splicing with a Wire Nut

- Remove the insulation from the end of the conductors and place the ends together **(Figure 6-F-6a)**. It is not necessary to twist the ends of the conductors together.

- Place the wire nut over the conductors and twist clockwise until it becomes snug. **(Figure 6-F-6b)**. Do not overtighten.

- The completed splice should be secure and have no bare wire showing past the opening of the wire nut **(Figure 6-F-6c)**.

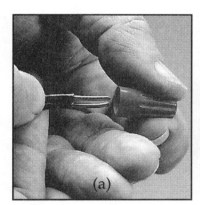
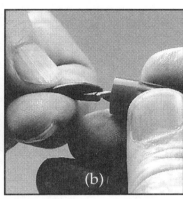
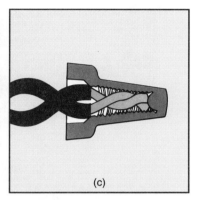

Figure 6-F-6a. Place the connector over the conductors.

Figure 6-F-6b. Twist the connector until snug.

Figure 6-F-6c. The completed connection.

▲ Splicing with a Crimped Connector

- After removing the insulation, place the connector over the ends of the conductors **(Figure 6-F-7a)**. Make sure no bare wire is exposed.

- Using a crimping tool suitable for making the connection, squeeze the connector until the connection feels solid and snug **(Figure 6-F-7b)**.

- The finished splice should appear as shown in **(Figure 6-F-7c)**.

Author's Note: Always check local codes before using crimped connectors for conductor splices.

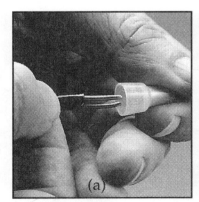
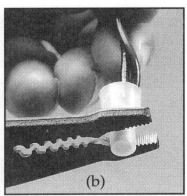
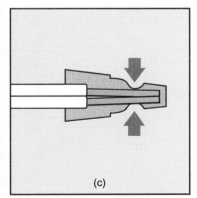

Figure 6-F-7a. Place the connector over the conductors.

Figure 6-F-7b. Squeeze the connector with a crimping tool until tight.

Figure 6-F-7c. The completed connection.

▲ Splicing with a Split -Bolt Connector

Split-bolt connectors are usually selected for use when splicing larger conductors such as No. 8 AWG through No. 4/0 AWG sizes. Usually only two conductors may be connected using a split-bolt connector.

To make a splice using a split-bolt connector, place the two, bare conductor ends in the connector **(Figure 6-F-8a)**. The nut is then tightened over the bolt until it becomes snug **(Figure 6-F-8b)**. The connection is then wrapped with electrical tape to the same thickness as the conductor insulation **(Figure 6-F-8c)**.

Author's Note:
Never splice more conductors than the split-bolt connector is designed to splice. It is rare that a splitbolt connector will accommodate more than 2 conductors.

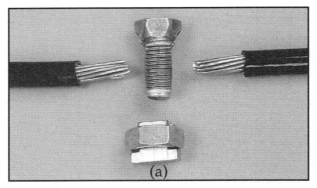

Figure 6-F-8a. *Remove the insulation from each conductor.*

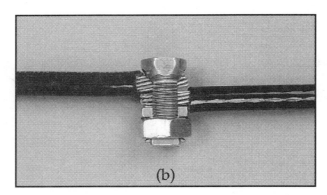

Figure 6-F-8b. *Place the split- bolt over the conductor ends and tighten the nut until snug.*

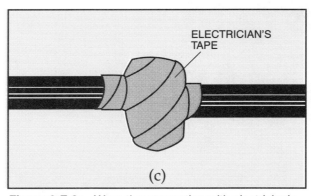

Figure 6-F-8c. *Wrap the connection with electrician's tape.*

Receptacles

Receptacles— along with switches—are easily the most recognizable parts of the residential electrical wiring system **(Figure 7-1)**. These are the electrical devices which are used every day in our homes and work places that give us convenient access to the electrical system.

In this chapter you will learn about the parts that comprise a receptacle, the different types of receptacles, designer receptacles and how to select the right receptacle for the right job.

There are essentially two types of receptacles that are used for residential branch circuit installations. These are discussed under the following headings:

A. Receptacles for General Purpose and Small Appliance Circuits.

B. Receptacles for Large Appliance and Individual Equipment Circuits

Figure 7-1. *Receptacles give the homeowner convenient access to the electrical system.*

A. Receptacles for General Purpose & Small Appliance Circuits

The most common type of receptacle used in residential installations for general purpose circuits is the **duplex receptacle.**

Figure 7-A-1 illustrates the different parts of a typical duplex receptacle and where each is located on the receptacle. The duplex receptacle consists of two halves, each designed to receive a three-contact plug. Each half is equipped with a **short contact,** which receives the hot conductor, and a **long contact,** which receives the grounded circuit conductor. Each half also has a **U-shaped grounding contact** which receives the grounding conductor.

Each half of the receptacle is also equipped with a **silver** screw terminal and a **brass** screw terminal for conductor connections. A **green grounding screw terminal** is usually located on the lower half of the receptacle.

Other parts of the typical duplex receptacle are:

- **Connecting tabs** - located between the two halves of the device. These allow the receptacle to used in a variety of installation configurations.

- **Mounting straps** - located at the top and bottom of the receptacle and are used to attach the device to the outlet box.

- **Amperage and Voltage rating** - indicates the maximum voltage and amperage rating for the receptacle. These may be located on the front or back of the device.

- **UL Label (Underwriters Laboratories)** - insures the receptacle meets industry standards.

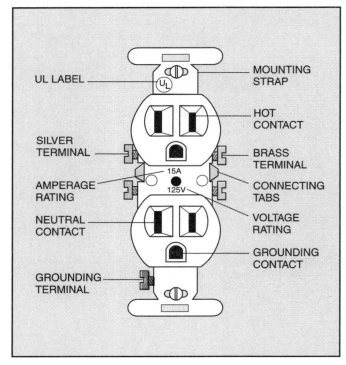

Figure 7-A-1. *Parts of a standard duplex receptacle.*

The back of the receptacle also contains information that should be checked before installation (**Figure 7-A-2**):

- **Push-in fittings** - used when back wiring a receptacle. The word "white" will usually appear on the side of the receptacle that receives the grounded circuit conductor.

- **Strip Gauge** - used to measure the correct amount of insulation to be removed from the conductors.

- **Conductor Ratings** - indicates the maximum conductor size to be used with the receptacle. Most common duplex receptacles are rated for No. 14 AWG or No. 12 AWG.

    Other markings which may appear on either the front or back of the receptacle, or in the installation instructions may include:

- **Copper Marking (CU)** - indicates the receptacle may be used only with copper conductors.

- **CU- Clad ONLY** - indicates the receptacle may be used only with copper - clad aluminum conductors.

- **CO/ALR** - indicates the receptacle may be used with either copper or copper clad aluminum conductors.

    Note: The NEC® no longer permits the use of receptacles marked AL/CU (Aluminum or Copper).

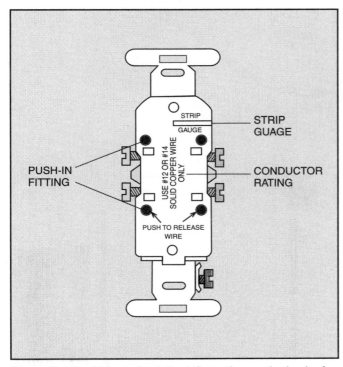

Figure 7-A-2. *Always check the information on the back of the receptacle before installation.*

■ Back-Wired Duplex Receptacles

A typical duplex receptacle, in addition to the mechanical terminal screws located on either side of the receptacle, is also equipped with **terminal holes** (also called **push-in terminals**) located on the back of the device **(Figure 7-A-3)**. These push-in terminals allow the device to be "backwired." While the NEC® approves the use of back wired receptacles it also states that back-wired receptacles <u>shall not</u> be the means for continuing a circuit. It states that backwired receptacles be used only to terminate a conductor. To continue a circuit conductor, splicing should be accomplished by using a pigtail and wire nut connection and all splices should always comply with NEC® requirements.

How to connecting a back-wired receptacle will be discussed in Chapter 8, ***Installing Branch Circuits***

NEC® References
For more on
backwired
receptacles, see
NEC® Articles
110-14
300-13b

Author's Note:
Although permitted
for use by the
NEC®, back-wired
receptacles may not
be permitted by
some local codes.

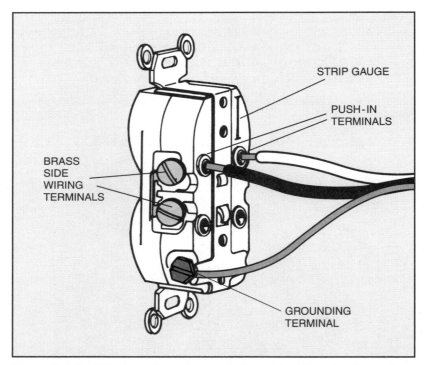

Figure 7-A-3. *A duplex receptacle may be back-wired by using the push-in terminals located on the back of the receptacle.*

■ Split-Wired, Duplex Receptacles

A standard duplex receptacle is equipped with two outlets and two sets of terminals. When the receptacle is used normally in the circuit run, both outlets are on the same circuit.

A **split-wired receptacle** is created from a standard duplex receptacle by removing the **connector tab** between the **brass** terminals **(Figure 7-A-4)**. Removing the connector tab "splits" the receptacle into separate outlets. Each half can then be wired to perform separate functions.

For example, you may wish to control a lamp by a wall switch. It can be connected to control one-half of the receptacle. The other half of the receptacle could be wired to remain constantly energized. This portion of the receptacle can be used for items such as electric clocks or other appliances which you wish to run constantly and without interruption.

Dividing the upper and lower receptacle outlets also helps prevent the possibility of overloading a single circuit. There may be several situations where two separate circuits from a single duplex receptacle is desirable. One example might be in a kitchen appliance circuit. You may also wish to use a split-wired receptacle in a shop area where there is always a danger of accidentally overloading a circuit.

Author's Note: When creating a split-wired duplex receptacle, the brass tab is usually removed; the silver tab remains intact and serves as a common neutral serving both halves of the receptacle.

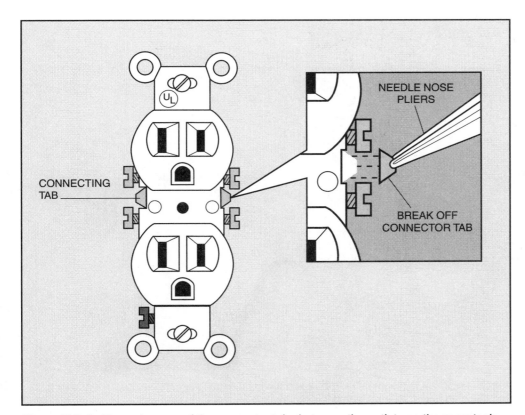

Figure 7-A-4. *Removing one of the connector tabs between the outlets on the receptacle creates a split-wired duplex receptacle. Split-wiring creates separate circuits on the upper and lower receptacle outlets.*

■ GFCI Duplex Receptacles

Ground Fault Circuit Interrupters (GFCIs), in addition to their use as duplex receptacles, also perform a special safety function in the circuit.

The NEC® requires GFCI use where dampness or water may exist in locations such as in bathrooms, kitchens, unfinished basements, crawl spaces, garages, wet bars, sinks and all outdoor locations.

NEC® Reference
For more on GFCI
receptacles, see
NEC® Article
210-8a

The GFCI receptacle can be used as a protection device in a single location (outlet), or may be installed to so that it will protect all receptacles following the GFCI on the circuit (connected downstream).

The GFCI duplex receptacle is configured much like the standard duplex receptacle—with a couple of notable exceptions. The GFCI is equipped with a **reset** and **test** button located on its front side **(Figure 7-A-5a)**. These are used for testing the receptacle and for resetting the receptacle after it has been tripped. It is also equipped with a grounding screw terminal.

Stamped on the upper back portion of the GFCI receptacle **(Figure 7-A-5b)** is the markings "LOAD," "HOT" and "WHITE" indicating the terminals for the black and neutral conductors. The marking, "LINE", appears on the lower half of the receptacle along with the markings "HOT" and "WHITE" indicating the hot and neutral terminal connections.

How GFCIs are installed in a circuit is discussed in Chapter 14, *Ground Fault Circuit Interrupters.*

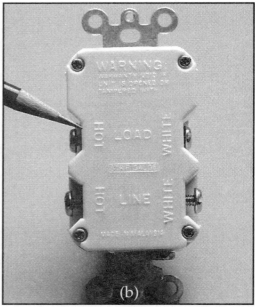

Figure 7-A-5. *(a) GFCI receptacles are equipped with test and reset buttons. (b) Check the information on the back of a GFCI receptacle for installation information.*

Types of Receptacles

Receptacles are available in a variety of styles and designs for most electrical needs in today's modern homes. Shown below are examples of receptacle types commonly used in residential electrical installations **(Figures 7-A-6)**.

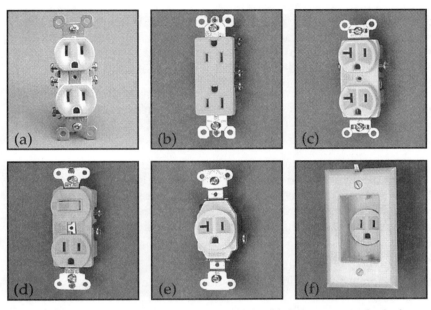

Figure 7-A-6. *(a) A standard duplex receptacle. (b) A decorator style duplex receptacle. (c) A 20-ampere duplex receptacle. (d) A combination switch/ receptacle. (e) A single, 20-ampere receptacle. (f) A clock receptacle.*

Receptacle Coverplates

Receptacle coverplates are designed to provide safety for both indoor and outdoor protection and to make the installation both functional and aesthetically pleasing to the eye. **Figure 7-A-7** shows examples typical receptacle coverplates. **Figure 7-A-8** shows a receptacle cover that allows the receptacle to ´ remain in use while also receiving weather protection.

Figure 7-A-7. *Examples of receptacle coverplates.*

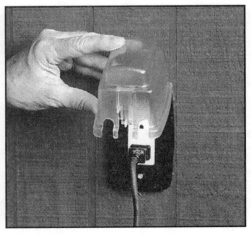

Figure 7-A-8. *A weather-proof receptacle coverplate.*

B. Large Appliance & Individual Equipment Receptacles

Receptacles for individual equipment and large appliance circuits differ from the typical duplex receptacles because they are intended to serve only one appliance or piece of equipment. Because of their specialized use, they have only one set of contacts rather than the two found on the duplex receptacle **(Figure 7-B-1)**. An exception to this statement are receptacles for clothes washers. Although clothes washers may be considered as a large appliances or individual equipment, they may be installed on an individual 120-volt circuit using a standard duplex receptacle. Appliances may be classified into three groups:

(1) Portable Appliances - small appliances such as coffee makers, mixers, blenders that may be plugged into a 20-ampere,120-volt circuits. They do not require special receptacles or plug-and-cord assemblies.

(2) Stationary Appliances - appliances that the home owner may move from one residence to another. These include self-contained ranges, clothes washers and dryers, window air conditioners, etc. Because they require large amounts of electrical current, these appliances are connected to the appliance circuit with receptacles and power cords with plugs designed specifically for that use.

(3) Fixed Appliances - appliances and large equipment that are permanently installed in the residence. The conductors used for connecting these appliances are usually hardwired from the appliance terminal block directly to its circuit breaker in the SEP. Fixed appliances may include built-in ovens, counter cook tops, trash compactors, garbage disposals, water heaters and heating and cooling systems.

NEC® References
For more appliance receptacles, see NEC® Articles
210-50a
220-4c
220-17
220-18

NEC® References
For more on kitchen range and clothes dryer installations, see NEC® Articles
250-140
250-134
250-138

(a)   (b)

Figure 7-B-1. *(a) Duplex receptacles are used for smaller, portable appliances. (b) Stationary and fixed appliances require larger, single receptacles designed to accommodate the larger load requirements.*

Self-contained kitchen range and clothes dryers are commonly installed using single receptacles dedicated for use with each appliance. They are available in two types: **flush mounted (Figure 7-B-2a)**, normally used in new construction, and **surface mounted,** used for mounting directly on finished wall surfaces **(Figure 7-B-2b)**.

Since 1996, the NEC® has required that kitchen ranges and dryers installed in new construction must use four- conductor installations. Prior to 1966, three conductor installations were permitted in new construction. Today, three conductor installations are allowed only in existing wiring systems installed prior to the NEC® change. Below are examples of three and four-conductor receptacles for ranges **(Figure 7-B-3)** and clothes dryers **(Figure 7-B-4)**.

Figure 7-B-2. *Receptacle types. (a) A flush-mounted. (b) A surface mounted.*

Figure 7-B-3. *Three and four-conductor range receptacles .*

Figure 7-B-4. *Three and four-conductor dryer receptacles.*

Kitchen ranges require heavy-duty, 50-ampere, 250-volt receptacles and plug-and-cord assemblies such as the one shown below in **Figure 7-B-5** .

Clothes dryers require heavy-duty, 30-ampere, 250-volt receptacles. **Figure 7-B-6** shows a four -conductor plug-and-cord assembly of the type required by the NEC® for all new residential installations.

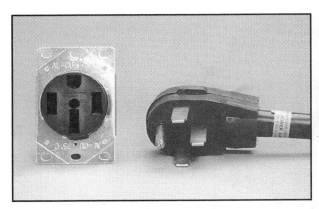

Figure 7-B-5. *A four-conductor, flush mounted range receptacle and plug assembly.*

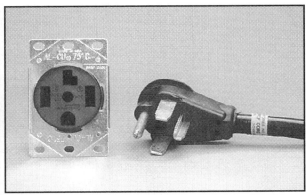

Figure 7-B-6. *A four -conductor, flush mounted clothes dryer receptacle and plug assembly.*

Figure 7-B-7 illustrates the letter designations for a four-conductor (pole) clothes dryer plug:

- The letter **"G"** indicates the equipment grounding terminal.

- The letter **"W"** indicates the white or grounded circuit conductor terminal.

- The letters **"X", "Y"** and **"Z"** indicate the ungrounded circuit conductor terminals. Conductor insulation colors are black and/or red for receptacles containing two or three terminals.

- Unmarked receptacle terminals are connected to ungrounded (hot) conductors.

Author's Note:
You should always consult the NEMA receptacle and plug configuration tables to help you determine the type of receptacle you will need.

While four-prong (pole) dryer and kitchen range receptacles may appear the same, they are easily distinguished by the shape of their grounding contacts. A dryer plug and receptacle is equipped with an L-shaped grounding contact **(Figure 7-B-8a)**. A range plug and receptacle is equipped with a straight grounding contact **(Figure 7-B-8b)**.

The **National Electrical Manufacturing Association (NEMA)** provides a complete list of general purpose plugs and receptacle configurations for residential wiring. A partial list is illustrated in **Table 7-1**. All devices are listed by the Underwriters Laboratories and are universally accepted by the electrical industry.

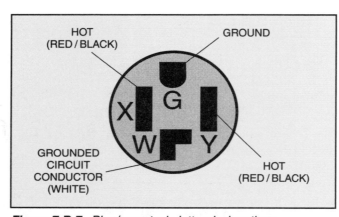

Figure 7-B-7. *Plug/receptacle letter designations.*

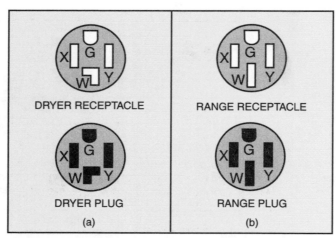

Figure 7-B-8. *(a) A clothes dryer receptacle and plug configuration. (b) A range receptacle and plug configuration.*

Table 7-1
NEMA Configurations for Straight Blade Plugs and Receptacles

NEMA No.		15 Ampere		20 Ampere		30 Ampere		50 Ampere		60 Ampere	
		Receptacle	Plug	Receptacle	Plug	Receptacle	Plug	Receptacle	Plug	Receptacle	Plug
2-Pole 2-Wire	**1** 125V	1-15R	1-15P								
	2 250V		2-15P	2-20R	2-20P	2-30R	2-30P				
2-Pole 3-Wire Grounding	**5** 125V	5-15R	5-15P	5-20R	5-20P	5-30R	5-30P	5-50R	5-50P		
	6 250V	6-15R	6-15P	6-20R	6-20P	6-30R	6-30P	6-50R	6-50P		
3-Pole 3-Wire	**7** 277V AC	7-15R	7-15P	7-20R	7-20P	7-30R	7-30P	7-50R	7-50P		
	10 125/250V			10-20R	10-20P	10-30R	10-30P	10-50R	10-50P		
3-Pole 4-Wire Grounding	**11** 3Ø 250V	11-15R	11-15P	11-20R	11-20P	11-30R	11-30P	11-50R	11-50P		
	14 125/250V	14-15R	14-15P	14-20R	14-20P	14-30R	14-30P	14-50R	14-50P	14-60R	14-60P
4-Pole 4-Wire	**15** 3Ø 250V	15-15R	15-15P	15-20R	15-20P	15-30R	15-30P	15-50R	15-50P	15-60R	15-60P
	18 3ØY 120/208V	18-15R	18-15P	18-20R	18-20P	18-30R	18-30P	18-50R	18-50P	18-60R	18-60P

Notes

Installing Branch Circuits

Installing branch circuits can be accomplished by using an approved receptacle and plug-and-cord assembly or by **"hardwiring"** directly to the overcurrent protection device in the SEP or subpanel. Branch circuits may be installed in a variety of options to a to achieve a desired result. The procedures for branch circuit installations discussed in this chapter are representative and consistent with those used for those in a typical residential wiring system.

It is important to remember that conductor connections must be made properly if the circuit is to function **(Figure 8-1)**. This means that all terminal and conductor connections must be installed to function properly for many years of trouble-free service. Problems are likely to occur with receptacles that are installed with poor connections. At best, poor workmanship could mean the circuit might work improperly—or not at all—and could result in great expense for the homeowner to correct the problem. At worst, it could result in devastation to life and property. Good workmanship should be practiced not only for reasons of professional liability— but also for professional pride.

In this chapter you will learn how to install circuits by:

A. Installing Standard Duplex Receptacles

B. Installing Small Appliance and Individual Branch Circuits.

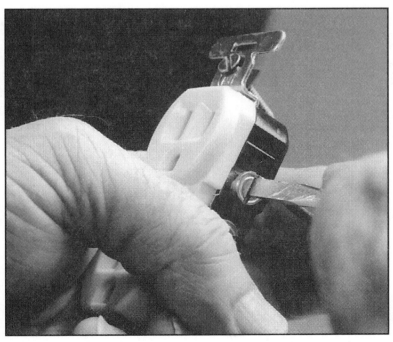

Figure 8-1. *For trouble free service, electrical connections must be properly installed.*

Before connecting a receptacle — or any electrical device—to a circuit, always check the device to make sure it is properly rated for its designated use. Make sure that you are using only listed receptacles.

Most receptacles used in today's newer homes are rated for either 15 or 20 ampere branch circuits. They are usually rated and labeled for use with copper (CU) conductors only. Manufacturers place this information directly on the device and/or in the installation instructions that accompany the product.

Once you have determined the proper rating and type of device to install, you must learn a few simple procedures to make sure it is installed correctly. A terminal screw that is not properly tightened, or a conductor that is improperly looped under a terminal screw will likely cause problems later. **Figure 8-2** illustrates a few basic steps that you can follow that will help ensure that your terminal connections will always be correct.

Author's Note:
Always practice good workmanship when installing conductors to any electrical device.

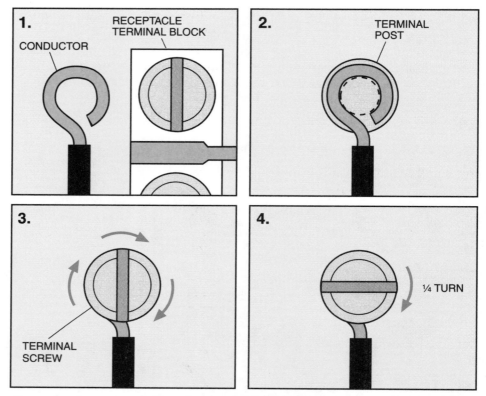

Figure 8-2. Steps for properly installing terminal connections. 1. Make a loop at the end of the conductor. 2. Place the loop around the post on the terminal screw. 3. Tighten the terminal screw until snug against the terminal contact plate. 4. Make an additional 1/4 turn .

A. Installing Duplex Receptacles

The basic procedures for connecting conductors to a duplex receptacle are illustrated in **Figures 8-A-1** below and **8-A-2** , page 126.

▦ Installing Duplex Receptacles (Nonmetallic Device Box)

- Remove approximately **5/8-inch** insulation from both insulated conductors **(Figure 8-A-1a)**.

- Using an electrician's tool or needle-nose pliers, make a loop at the end of the black, white, and grounding conductors **(Figure 8-A-1b)**.

- Place the looped end of the **black (hot)** conductor under the **brass** screw terminal on the receptacle. Pull the loop snug around the screw terminal and tighten with a screwdriver **(Figure 8-A-1c)**. Insert the looped end of the **white** conductor under the **silver** screw terminal on the opposite side of the switch and tighten. No bare wire should be exposed.

- Complete the installation by connecting the **grounding** conductor to the **green** terminal on the receptacle **(Figure 8-A-1d)**.

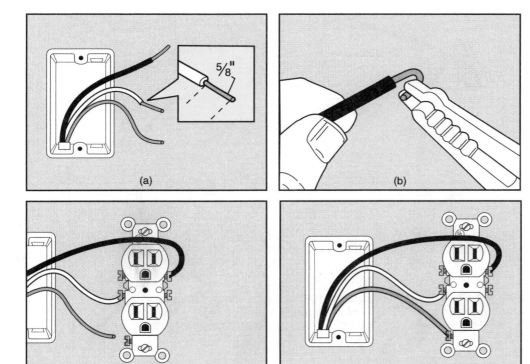

Author's Note:
Cable clamps and cable connectors are not required when installing NM cable in nonmetallic boxes.

Figure 8-A-1. *Installing conductors on a duplex receptacle in a nonmetallic device box. (a) Remove the conductor insulation. (b) Make a loop at the end of the conductors. (c) Connect the black conductor the brass terminal and the white conductor to the silver terminal. (d) Connect the grounding conductor to the receptacle ground.*

■ Installing Duplex Receptacles (Metallic Device Box)

When installing receptacles in metallic outlet boxes, the procedure differ from those of nonmetallic boxes. The NEC® requires that the receptacle be grounded to the box with the equipment grounding conductor. This can be accomplished with the following steps **(Figure 8-A-2)**:

- Use **(one)** 4 to 6-inch length of **bare** or **green insulated** jumper conductor (also called a pigtail) and strip approximately 5/8- inch insulation from its end **(Figure 8-A-2a)**.

- Use a **(second)** 4 to 6-inch length of grounding conductor (green insulated or bare jumper wire), strip the insulation from each end and connect it to the **green grounding terminal** on the **receptacle (Figure 8-A-2b)**.

- Secure the ends of the power supply cable grounding conductor and the two jumper conductors together with a wire nut **(Figure 8-A-2c)**.

- Connect the **white** conductor to the **silver** receptacle terminal and the **black** conductor to the **brass** receptacle terminal **(Figure 8-A-2d)**.

Author's Note:
Cable clamps and cable connectors are required when installing NM cable in metallic boxes.

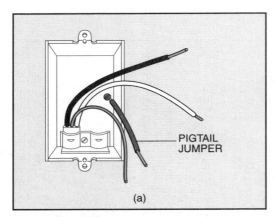
(a)

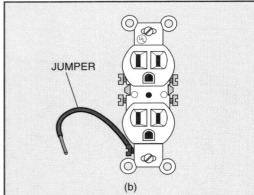
(b)

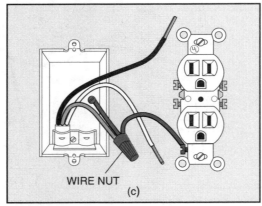
(c)

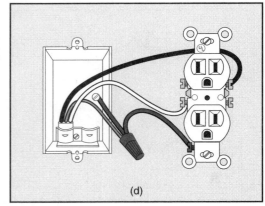
(d)

Figure 8-A-2. *Installing conductors on a duplex receptacle in a metallic device box. (a) Install a pigtail grounding conductor. (b) Connect a pigtail grounding conductor to the receptacle ground. (c) Connect both pigtail grounding conductors to the equipment ground. (d) Connect the black and white conductors to the receptacle.*

■ Installing Additional Duplex Receptacles

Adding additional duplex receptacles to the circuit run can easily be accomplished by following a few simple steps shown in **Figure 8-A-3.**

❶ Outlet #1 Connections

- Using a 4 to 6-inch piece of **white jumper (pigtail)** conductor as a jumper conductor, connect the **white** conductor in the power source cable and the white conductor in cable #1 to the top **silver** terminal on the receptacle.

- Using a **black jumper** conductor, connect both **hot (black)** conductors to the top **brass** terminal on the receptacle.

- Using an insulated **green** or **bare** jumper conductor connect the grounding conductors from both cables to the **green grounding terminal** on the receptacle.

❷ Outlet #2 Connections

- Make the connections for outlet #2 identical to those for outlet #1

❸ Outlet #3 Connections

- Make the connections to outlet #3 as shown.

Authors Note: Because this installation uses nonmetallic boxes, an equipment grounding conductor is not required to be installed to the box.

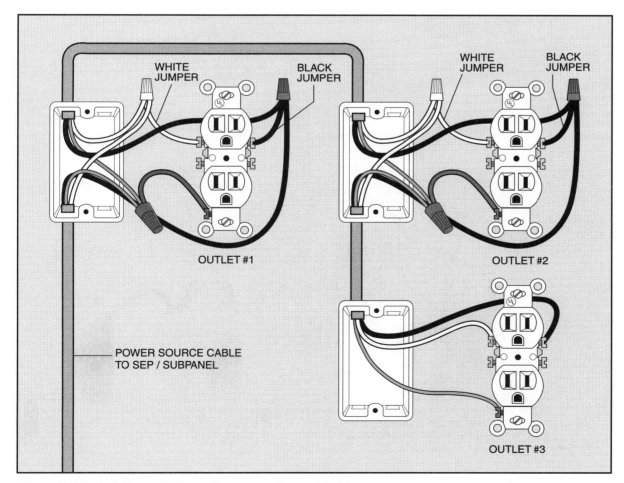

Figure 8-A-3. *Installing multiple duplex receptacles in a circuit.*

■ Installing Back-Wired Duplex Receptacles

When making the decision to use a back-wired duplex receptacle, you must be aware of certain restrictions where they <u>may</u> or <u>may not</u> be used. The NEC® code states that receptacles or other devices <u>shall not</u> be the means for continuing a circuit in a **multi-wire circuit**. Back-wired receptacles can be used only to terminate a conductor—not to continue the circuit.

To connect a back-wired duplex receptacle **(Figure 8-A-4)**:

- Strip the **black** and **white** conductor insulation to the correct length. You may use the strip gauge located on the back of the receptacle to determine the correct length of insulation to remove. The strip gauge indicates the depth of the hole in the receptacle.

NEC® Reference
For more on back wired duplex receptacles, see NEC Article 300-13b

- Insert the **white** conductor into one of the holes located nearest the silver terminals. On most receptacles designed for back-wiring, these holes are noted by the word **"white"** printed on the back of the receptacle. On some receptacles, the connection is considered complete simply by inserting the conductor into the hole. On other types, even though the conductors are inserted through the holes in the back of the receptacle, the silver and brass terminal screws must be tightened to ensure that the connection is secure.

- Insert the **black** conductor into one of the holes nearest the **brass** terminals and opposite the **white** conductor just installed.

- Install the grounding conductor to the **green** grounding screw terminal on the receptacle.

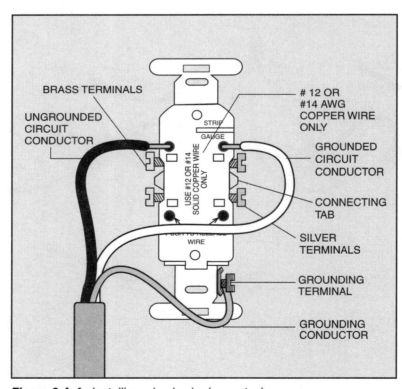

Figure 8-A-4. *Installing a back-wired receptacle.*

Installing Split-Wired Duplex Receptacles

Split-wired duplex receptacles are desirable when there is a desire to connect two circuits to one receptacle. Two options are typically used:

▼ Split-Wired Option #1

This option requires (2) two-conductor cables with ground. Each cable connects one-half of the receptacle directly to the overcurrent protection at the SEP or subpanel **(Figure 8-A-5)**. The NEC® requires that both circuits be protected by (1) double- pole circuit breaker or by (2) single-pole circuit breakers equipped with a handle tie. This overcurrent protection system ensures that both hot conductors are disconnected at the same time. Failure to provide this protection could result in severe shock. To connect the receptacle using this option:

- Remove the tab between the two brass terminals on the receptacle. The two outlets are no longer connected. **NOTE: It is _not_ necessary to remove the tab between the silver terminals.**

- Connect the **white** conductor from each cable to the **silver** screw terminals on the receptacle.

- Connect the **black (hot)** conductor from each cable to the **brass** screw terminals on the receptacle.

- Connect the receptacle and the metallic box to the grounding conductor using (2) 4 to 6-inch jumper conductors (pigtails) and a wire nut.

NEC® Reference
For more on splitwired receptacles, see NEC® Article 210-4

Author's Note: Caution! 240-volts exist between black conductors in a split-wired installation.

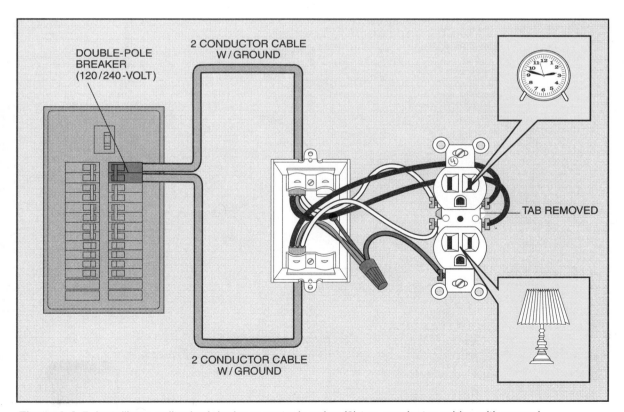

Figure 8-A-5. *Installing a split-wired duplex receptacle using (2) two-conductor cables with ground.*

▼ Split-Wired Option #2

This option requires a single three-conductor cable with ground installed as a 120/240-volt circuit. Each half of the receptacle carries a 120-volt circuit connected at the SEP by a double-pole circuit breaker **(Figure 8-A-6)**. The load becomes balanced between the two circuits and the danger of an overload on the white conductor is avoided. This is an example of a **multi-wire circuit**. To connect the receptacle using this optional method:

NEC® References For more on multiwire circuit installations, see NEC® Articles 210-4 300-13 b

- Remove the tab between the **brass screw** terminals on the receptacle **(Figure 8-A-6)**. It is not necessary to remove the tab between the **silver** terminals.

- Connect the **white** conductor to one of the **silver** screw terminals on the receptacle.

- Connect the **hot (black)** conductor to one of the **brass** screw terminals on the receptacle.

- Connect the other **hot (red)** conductor to the other **brass** screw terminal on the receptacle.

- Connect the grounding conductor to the **green** grounding screw on the receptacle.

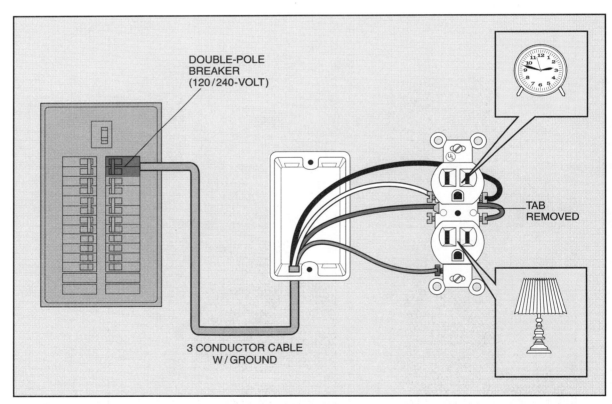

Figure 8-A-6. *Installing a split-wired duplex receptacle using a three-conductor cable with ground.*

Completing the Installation

After you have made all the necessary receptacle connections on the circuit, you will need to complete the installation by pushing the receptacles into the outlet boxes, and applying the cover plates. This step usually takes place after all work has been done to the wall surface. This is a very simple process, however it must be done with care not to damage the wall surface or loosen the receptacle/conductor connections. To properly complete the installation, proceed with the following steps:

- Check all connections **(Figure 8-A-7a)**.

- Place the receptacle into the outlet box by carefully folding the conductors accordion style and pushing them back into the outlet box **(Figure 8-A-7b)**.

- Fasten the receptacle to the outlet box **(Figure 8-A-7c)**. The receptacle should be mounted so that it is visually aligned. If the outlet box has not been installed properly, you may adjust the receptacle alignment by adjusting the mounting screws at the top and bottom of the receptacle.

- Attach the receptacle cover plate **(Figure 8-A-7d)**. Insert the center screw using a hand held screwdriver. Take care not to break the cover plate by overtightening the screw.

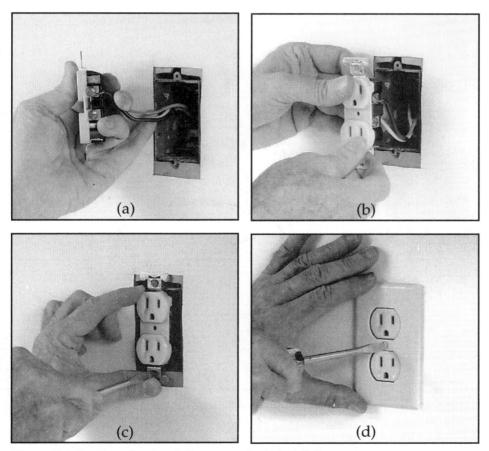

Figure 8-A-7. *Steps for completing a receptacle installation.*

B. Installing Small & Large Appliance Branch Circuits

The procedures for connecting small and large appliances and equipment to their circuits may be accomplished in two ways:

(1) Receptacles with plug-and-cord assemblies.

(2) Installing electrical cable by hardwiring directly from the appliance terminal block to the overcurrent protection device.

To determine the requirements for small appliance and individual branch circuits, refer to **Table 8-1**.

Installations for both kitchen ranges and clothes dryers in new construction are required to use four-conductor receptacles and plug-and-cord assemblies **(Figure 8-B-1)**. They may also use four-conductor cable hardwired directly to the overcurrent protection device at the panelboard **(Figure 8-B-2)**. **In** four-conductor installations, the neutral and grounding conductors are separate. Grounding conductors for ranges are not required to be insulated **(Figure 8-B-3)**. For dryer connections, the grounding conductor must be fully insulated and green in color **(Figure 8-B-4)**.

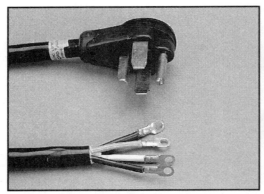

Figure 8-B-1. *A four-conductor kitchen range plug-and-cord assembly.*

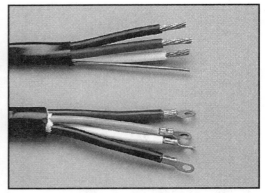

Figure 8-B-2. *Four-conductor cable.*

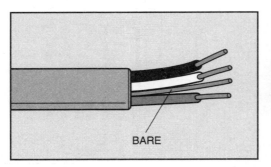

BARE

Figure 8-B-3. *Equipment grounds for ranges are not required to be insulated.*

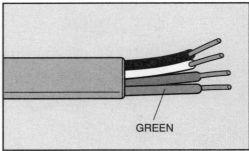

GREEN

Figure 8-B-4. *Equipment grounds for clothes dryers must be green.*

■ Range & Dryer Circuit Installations (Receptacle and Plug-and-Cord Assembly)

Range and clothes dryer installations made in new construction (prior to 1996) typically use surface or flush mounted receptacle connections and the NEC® required four-conductor plug-and-cord assembly. For existing installations, those installed prior to 1966, a three-conductor assembly may still be used. Remember, installations for ranges and dryers each require different ampere ratings and conductor sizes. See **Table 8-1** page 134, for the correct overcurrent protection rating and conductor size for ranges and dryers. When in doubt, you should also consult the the NEC® and the manufacturer's installation requirements.

Figure 8-B-5 illustrates the connections for range and clothes dryer receptacles using a four-conductor (three conductors plus a grounding conductor) plug-andcord assembly and a flush mounted receptacle.

- Connect the **white** conductor to the **"W"** receptacle terminal.

- Connect the **black (hot)** conductor to the **"Y"** receptacle terminal.

- Connect the **red (hot)** conductor to the **"X "** receptacle terminal.

- Connect the **ground** conductor to the **"G"** receptacle terminal.

NEC® References
For more on range and dryer installation requirements, see NEC® Articles
210-19b
250-134
250-138
250-140

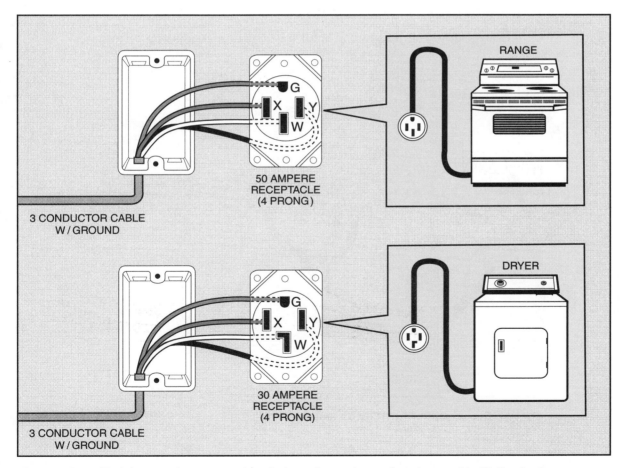

Figure 8-B-5. *(Top) four-conductor range installation using a plug-and-cord assembly. (Bottom) a four-conductor clothes dryer installation using a plug-and-cord assembly.*

■ Range & Dryer Hardwired Circuit Installations

Range and dryer circuits may also be connected by making the connections to the terminal block on the appliance and by hardwiring to the overcurrent protection device in the SEP or subpanel. **Figure 8-B-6 (Option #1)** illustrates range and dryer connections using a four-conductor installation. **Figure 8-B-7 (Option #2)** illustrates connections using an existing three-conductor installation.

NEC® References
For more on range and dryer installations, see NEC® Articles
250-134
250-138
250-140

- **Ranges**- range circuit installations require a #6 AWG, four-conductor cable and a minimum 50-ampere overcurrent protection device (circuit breaker)

- **Clothes Dryers** - clothes dryer circuit installations require a #10 AWG, four-conductor cable and a minimum 30-ampere overcurrent protection device (circuit breaker).

▲ (Option #1) Four Conductor Range & Dryer Circuit Installations

- Connect the **white** conductor to the **silver** screw terminal on the terminal block.

- Connect the **black (hot)** conductor to the **brass** screw terminal on the terminal block.

- Connect the **red (hot)** conductor to the other **brass** screw terminal on the terminal block.

- Connect the grounding conductor to the **green** grounding screw.

Figure 8-B-6. *Four-conductor range and dryer installations for terminal block and junction box connections.*

▲ (Option #2) Three Conductor Range & Dryer Circuit Installations

Although three-conductor installations for ranges and dryers have not been allowed by the NEC® in new construction since 1996, you are likely to encounter this problem when installing new ranges or dryers to an existing three-conductor system. The terminal block on each appliance is equipped from the manufacturer for either the newer, four-conductor system or the older, three-conductor system **(Figure 8-B-7)**. Whether hardwiring directly from the appliance to the panel board or a receptacle with plug-and cord assembly **(Figure 8-B-7 inset),** you should always follow the manufacturer's directions for installation.

- Connect the **black (hot)** conductor to the brass terminal screw on the block.

- Connect the **red (hot)** conductor to the other brass terminal screw.

- Connect the **white** conductor to the silver screw on the terminal block.

- Connect a **green** jumper conductor from the neutral terminal to the grounding terminal. Check to make sure the grounding terminal is bonded to the equipment frame. This jumper is usually installed at the factory, however, if it is not included, you must install it before the installation can be completed and safe to operate.

  NOTE: The jumper must be removed when making the installation in a four- conductor system.

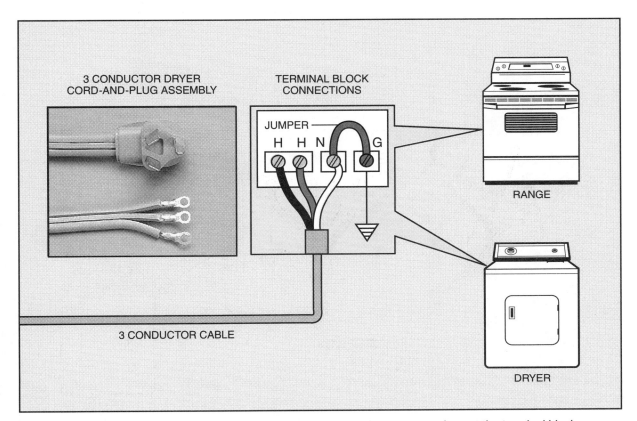

Figure 8-B-7. *Range and dryer installations illustrating three-conductor connections at the terminal block.*

■ Separate Oven & Cooktop Circuit Installations

The procedures for connecting circuits for separate ovens and cooktops are much like those for self-contained ranges and clothes dryers. They are usually made by connecting a cable to the terminal block on the appliance and then making additional connections in a junction box **(Figure 8-B-8)**. The procedure below is illustrated using nonmetallic sheathed cable and a nonmetallic junction box.

After the proper connections have been made to the terminal block on each appliance, the conductors for both appliances are spliced together within the junction box using wire nuts. These connections may be made with NM cable or by using **fleximetal conduit** supplied with the appliance by the manufacturer. When using this method of connection, a metallic junction box with the proper cable connectors is required.

With either method, a four-conductor cable must be used for the circuit. When the installation is made with fleximetal conduit, either nonmetallic sheathed cable or four, separate conductors may be used.

To determine the correct conductor size and overcurrent protection rating for separate ovens and cooktops, consult **Table 8-1** on page 134, the NEC® and the manufacturer's instructions. If you wish to connect the oven or cooktop using a plug and receptacle assembly, consult the NEMA table on page 111 to determine which type and amperage rating is recommended.

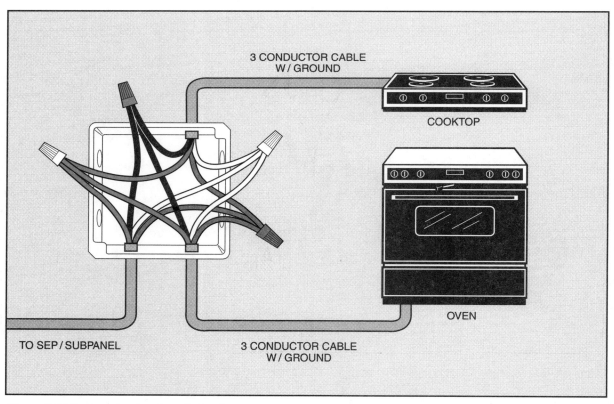

Figure 8-B-8. *Junction box installation for separate oven and cooktop unit.*

■ Water Heater Circuit Installations

Water heater circuit installations are usually made directly from the appliance terminal block to the overcurrent protection device in the SEP or subpanel **(Figure 8-B-9).** Most codes, state or local, require that connections be made within a junction box at least 12 or more inches from the appliance. These same codes may also require a disconnect be at the water heater as a safety precaution. The NEC® requires that water heater connections that are not visible from the overcurrent protection device at the subpanel or SEP, must have a disconnect located within 50 ft. of the appliance.

Water heaters operate at 240-volts and require either a #10-2 AWG cable with ground and a 30-ampere overcurrent protection device. They may also operate at 120-volts and require a #12-2, AWG cable with ground and a 20-ampere overcurrent device circuit breaker. Always consult the manufacturer's directions for the recommended overcurrent protection and conductor sizes or with your local code inspector. For a quick reference, see **Table 8-1,** page 134, to help you determine the requirements for water heater installations.

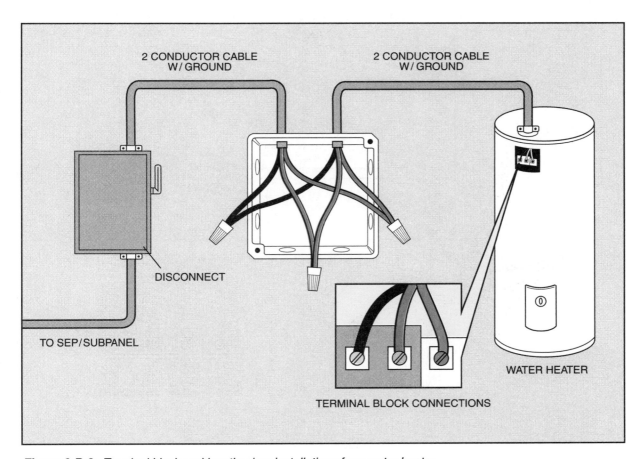

Figure 8-B-9. *Terminal block and junction box installations for a water heater.*

▪ Clothes Washer Circuit Installations

Most installations for clothes washers are generally made with a standard, 120-volt duplex receptacle, #12-2 AWG with ground cable/conductors and 20-ampere circuit breakers **(Figure 8-B-10)**. A special, single outlet receptacle may also be used if needed. It is important for you to remember that although a standard duplex receptacle may be used for the appliance connection, this installation is still considered a separate or individual circuit. No other appliance may be connected to this circuit. The NEC® requires that the receptacle for a clothes washer be located within 6 ft. of the appliance location because most washer plug-and-cord assemblies are 6 ft. long.

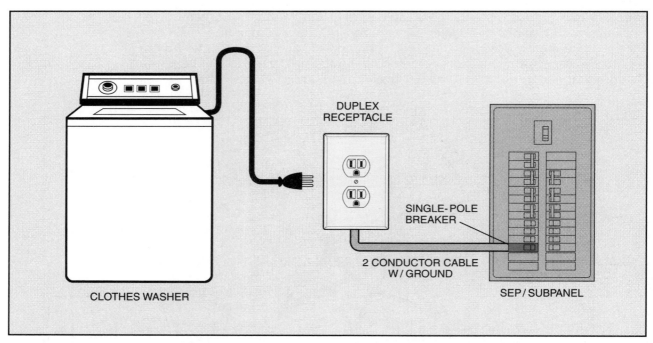

Figure 8-B-10. *Although clothes washers require only 120-volts and 20-ampere circuit breakers, they must be installed on individual circuits.*

NEC® References
For more on
clothes washer
installations, see
NEC® Articles
210-50c
210-52f
220-4c
220-16b

■ Garbage Disposal & Dishwasher Circuit Installations

There are three basic options for installing garbage disposals and dishwashers and each is illustrated in the following segment of this chapter.

The recommended conductor size for each of these installations is a #12-2 AWG with ground. A 20-ampere circuit breaker is required.

▼ (Option #1) Separate Circuit Installations

Figure **8-B-11a** illustrates a switch controlled garbage disposal connected to an individual circuit. Figure **8-B-11b** illustrates the junction box connections for hardwiring a dishwasher to an individual circuit.

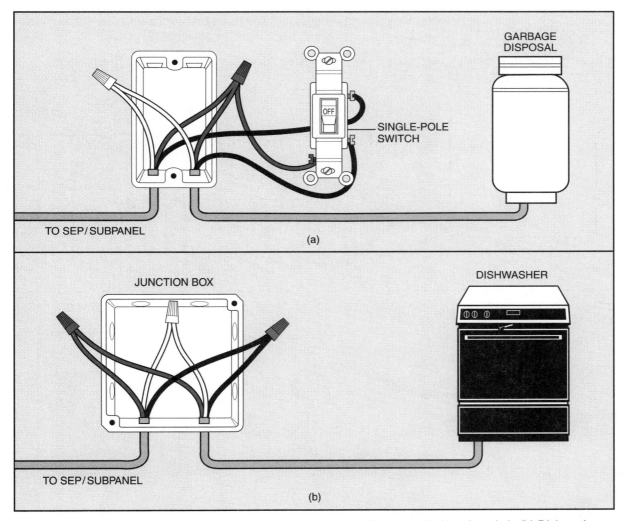

Figure 8-B-11. *Individual circuits for (a) A garbage disposal controlled by a single-pole switch. (b) Dishwasher connections installed in a junction box.*

▼ (Option #2) Split-Wired Duplex Receptacle Installations

Figure 8-B-12 illustrates the installation for a garbage disposal controlled by a single-pole switch and a dishwasher connected by a plug and cord assembly to an unswitched receptacle outlet.

- Remove the tab between the two **brass** screw terminals on the receptacle to create a split-receptacle. Select the portion of the receptacle you wish to use for the disposal plug-in.

- Connect the **white** conductor in the power source cable to one of the **silver** screw terminals on the on the receptacle.

- Connect the **black** conductor in the switch leg cable to one of the **brass screw** terminals on the receptacle and to the **brass** screw terminal on the switch.

- Using a wire nut, connect a **black jumper** conductor from the remaining **brass** screw terminal on the receptacle to the **black** conductor on the power source cable and to the **white** conductor in the switch leg cable.

- Using a pigtail jumper, connect the **grounding** conductor in the power source cable and the switch leg cable to the receptacle equipment ground.

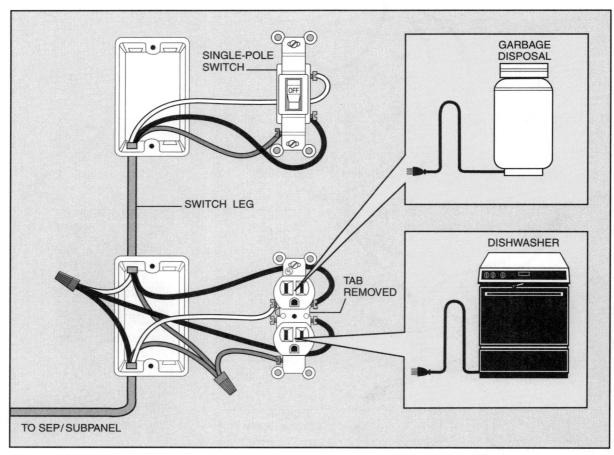

Figure 8-B-12. *Split-wired duplex receptacle installations for a garbage disposal and dishwasher. The garbage disposal is controlled by a single-pole switch installed to the top half of the receptacle. The lower half of the receptacle remains constantly energized and controls the dishwasher.*

▼ (Option #3) Junction Box Installations

Figure 8-B-13 illustrates a switch controlled garbage disposal and a dishwasher installed directly to the overcurrent device. Connections are made in a nonmetallic junction box.

❶ Switch Connections

* Make the necessary **white, black** and **grounding** conductor connections at the single-pole switch controlling the garbage disposal.

❷ Junction Box Connections

* Using a wire nut, connect the **black** conductors in cable #1 (switch leg) and cable #2.

* Using a wire nut, connect the **white** conductor in cable #1 (switch leg) to the **black** conductors in the power source cable and cable #3.

* Using a wire nut, connect the **white** conductors in cable #2, the power source cable and cable #3.

* Connect the cable **grounding** conductors in the junction box

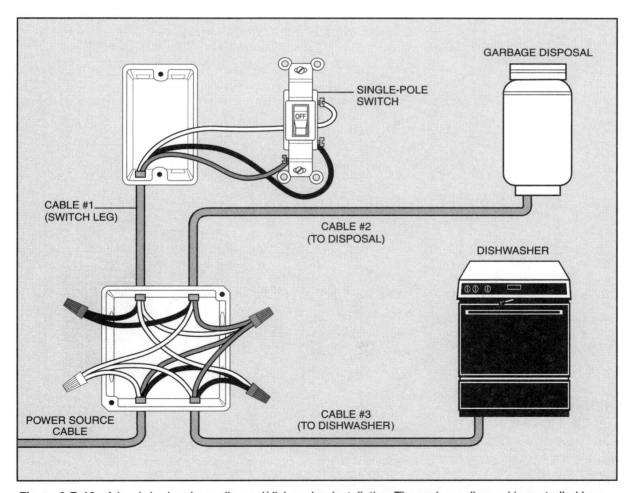

Figure 8-B-13. *A hardwired garbage disposal/dishwasher installation. The garbage disposal is controlled by a single -pole switch. The dishwasher is wired directly to the overcurrent protection device and remains constantly energized.*

■ Central Heating & Air Conditioning Circuit Installations

Electric central heating and air conditioning systems are one of the major electrical power consumers in residential housing and like all heavy users of electricity, they are installed on individual circuits. Normally, the electrical installer will provide the rough-in cable installation. Later, the heating/cooling technician will make the final connections.

NEC® Reference
For more on
heating and air
conditioning
installations
requirements, see
NEC® Articles
440-11
440-12
440-14

The nameplate located on the unit will contain branch circuit ratings, required cable and conductor sizes, overcurrent protection rating and the amperage and voltage rating for the unit. More information can be found in the manufacturer's installation and specification manual. Be sure to read these instructions and check with your local electrical inspector before proceeding with the installation of any electrical appliance or other electrical equipment.

Figure 8-B-14 illustrates a typical central heating and air conditioning system installation. The **compressor** (outdoor condensing unit) is usually located outside the residence. The **air handler** (blower fan), usually located inside the residence, may be rated for either 120 or 240-volt service. Good planning and wiring practice suggests that both units be installed as close as possible to the SEP or subpanel. The compressor unit requires a 240-volt overcurrent protection device and a 2-conductor cable with ground. The NEC® requires that a disconnect be located near the compressor unit when the equipment is not visible from the overcurrent protection device or is located more that 50 ft. from the SEP or subpanel.

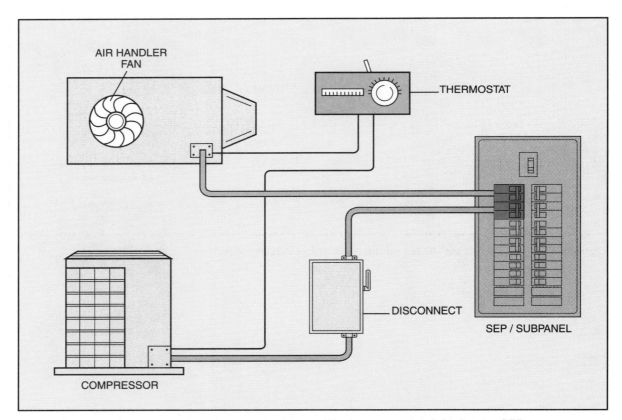

Figure 8-B-14. *A typical installation for a heating/air conditioning system hardwired to the SEP.*

■ Electric Heater Circuit Installations

Electric heaters for residential use will include sizes from electric furnaces large enough to heat an entire house to a small room heater. Bathroom wall heaters such as those indicated on the sample floor plan are typical of the smaller type electric heaters used in many homes **(Figure 8-B-15)**. Baseboard heating units controlled by thermostats are a common method of electric heating in many parts of the country. Electric heaters may operate at either 120-volt or 240-volt units.

The following steps are common for most electric heater installations:

- Determine the type and size of individual branch circuit required. This means selecting the proper cable and conductor size and the correct overcurrent protection device (circuit breaker).

- Install the unit on a separate (individual) circuit.

- When installing the heating unit, make sure the connections are made according to the manufacturer's instructions and specifications.

NEC® Reference
For more on electric heater installation requirements, see NEC® Article 424-9

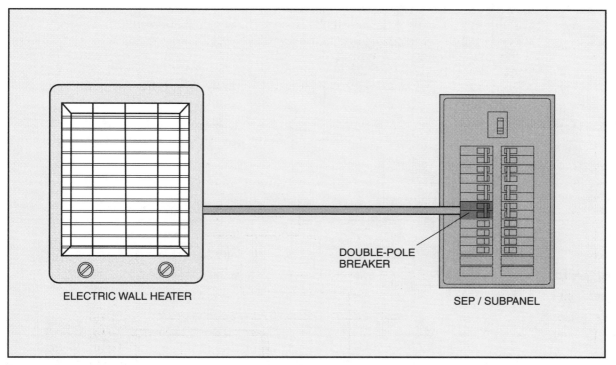

ELECTRIC WALL HEATER

DOUBLE-POLE BREAKER

SEP / SUBPANEL

Figure 8-B-15. *An electric wall heater hardwired to a double-pole breaker.*

Table 8-1
Circuit Requirements for Kitchen and Laundry Circuits
(Voltage, Conductor Sizes and Breaker Rating)

Kitchen Appliances	Voltage	Circuit Conductor Size	Breaker Rating	Circuit Type
Range	120-240	No. 6 AWG	50	Individual Circuit
Range Double Oven	120-240	No. 4 AWG	70	Individual Circuit
Built-in Oven	120-240	No. 10 AWG	30	Individual Circuit
Range Top	120-240	No. 8 AWG	40	Individual Circuit
Broiler/Roaster	120	No. 12 AWG	20	Small Appliance Circuit
Fry Pan	120	No. 12 AWG	20	Small Appliance Circuit
Coffee Maker	120	No. 12 AWG	20	Small Appliance Circuit
Portable Grill	120	No. 12 AWG	20	Small Appliance Circuit
Kitchen Receptacles	120	No. 12 AWG	20	2 Small Appliance Circuits (minimum)
Exhaust Fan	120	No. 12 AWG	20	General Purpose Lighting Circuit
Refrigerator	120	No. 12 AWG	20	Recommend Separate Circuit
Food Freezer	120	No. 12 AWG	20	Recommend Separate Circuit
Dishwasher	120	No. 12 AWG	20	Recommend Separate Circuit
Waste Disposal	120	No. 12 AWG	20	May combine with Dishwasher Circuit
Laundry Appliances				
Washer	120	No. 12 AWG	20	Separate Circuit
Dryer	120/240	No. 10 AWG	30	Individual Circuit
High Speed Dryer	120/240	No. 6 AWG	50	Individual Circuit
Clothes Iron	120	No. 12 AWG	20	May use Separate Washer Circuit
Water Heater	240	No. 10 AWG	30-40	Individual Circuit

Switches

9

In residential electrical systems, switches are used to control most lighting outlets and other applications such as switched appliances, switched-receptacles, motion switches and others. The most common type of switch used in residential wiring is the single-pole toggle switch like the one shown in **Figure 9-1**.

In this chapter, you will learn about the different types of switches commonly used in residential wiring systems. You will learn how they work, how to identify them, how to select the right switch for the right job and how to install them. Before you begin the installation of a switch — or any type of electrical device — always read the manufacturer's directions.

Switches are discussed under the following topics:

A. How Switches Work

B. Types of Switches

C. Examples of Common Switches

D. Installing Single-Pole Switches

E. Installing Switched-Duplex Receptacles

F. Installing Switched-Combination Receptacles

G. Installing Double-Pole Switches

H. Installing Dimmer Switches

I. Installing Ceiling Fan Switches

Figure 9-1. *Switches provide the homeowner with convenient access to the wiring system in the residence.*

A. How Switches Work

Switches, like receptacles, are designed to perform a specific function in controlling the electricity at the outlet. The parts of a single-pole switch and the function each performs is shown in **Figure (9-A-1)**. The NEC® does not require equipment grounding terminals on switches. However, they are commonly used and may be required by local codes. Safe wiring practice suggests that switches with grounding terminals be used whenever possible because they provide extra protection when installed in the electrical wiring system..

- **Switch Toggle** - controls switch to a"ON" or "OFF" position when moved up or down. When the switch is properly mounted, the "ON" marking on the toggle will be visible when the toggle is pushed to the "UP" position.

- **Screw Terminals** - screw connections for cable conductors. Screw terminal locations on the switch may vary depending on manufacturer. The top terminal on the switch is also known as the **line** or **input** terminal and the bottom terminal is know as the **load** terminal.

- **Grounding Screw Terminal** - provides connection for grounding conductor. Usually green in color. Location on switch varies.

- **Mounting Strap, Ears and Adjustment Screws** - used to fasten the switch to outlet box.

Switches, like receptacles, are usually stamped with amperage and voltage ratings, conductor AWG ratings and wire strip gauges. They may also be equipped with push-in fittings for back wiring applications.

Author's Note:
Always install a switch so that the words "On" and "Off" are oriented correctly.

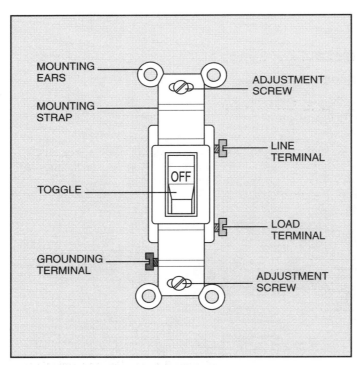

Figure 9-A-1. *Parts of a single-pole switch.*

How a Single-Pole Switch Works

A single-pole switch consists of a toggle switch, two external terminals and two internal contacts. How these contacts control power to the circuit is illustrated in **Figures 9-A-2 a,b and c.** When the switch toggle handle is pushed up to the "ON" position, the internal contacts are connected (made). Electricity passes through the switch to the fixture. The lighting fixture is now "ON".

When the switch toggle handle is pushed down to the "OFF" position, the internal contacts are broken and the electrical flow stops. The lighting fixture is now "OFF."

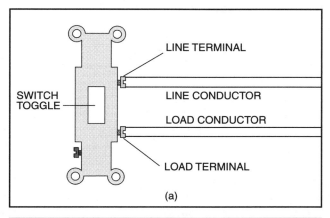

Figure 9-A-2a. Terminal connections for a single-pole switch.

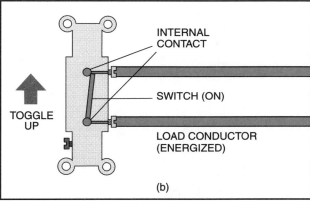

Figure 9-A-2b. Switch terminals are energized when the switch toggle is moved to "ON" position.

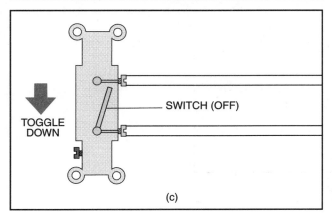

Figure 9-A-2c. Switch terminals are de-energized when the switch toggle is moved to "OFF" position.

B. Types of Switches

Switches used for most residential wiring installations come in four basic types. You must become familiar with each of these types and how to correctly install them.

- **Single-Pole Switches (Figure 9-B-1)** - most common type of switch. Generally used for controlling lighting and appliances from one source location. They may also be used to control from one to several lights on a circuit.

- **Double -Pole Switches (Figure 9-B-2)** - used for 240-volt switched circuits.

- **Three-Way Switches (Figure 9-B-3)** - used for controlling lighting outlets from two (2) separate locations.

- **Four-Way Switches (Figure 9-B-4)** - used in combination with three-way switches for controlling lighting from three (3) or more locations.

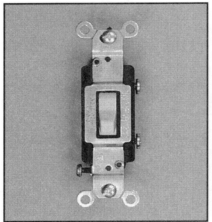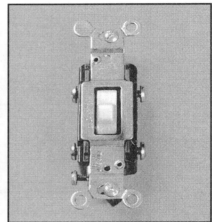

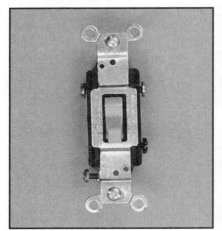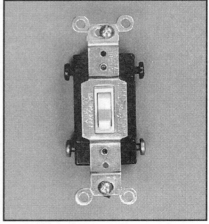

(Top left) Figure 9-B-1.
Example of a single-pole switch.

(Top right) Figure 9-B-2.
Example of a double-pole switch.

(Bottom left) Figure 9-B-3.
Example of a three-way switch.

(Bottom right) Figure 9-B-4.
Example of a four-way switch.

C. Examples of Common Switches

Switches come in a variety of styles and options for all applications and in designer/decorator colors for almost any need. **Figures 9-C-1a thru 9-C-1h** below shows examples of popular switch types and styles available at most electrical supply stores and home centers.

- **Standard Single-Pole Switch (Figure 9-C-1a)** - common switch type used in residential wiring.

- **Rocker Switch (Figure 9-C-1-b)** - decorator style switch

- **Push Button Switch with Movement Sensor (Figure 9-C-1c)** - can be adjusted to control on- off room lighting by movement.

- **Switch and Receptacle Combination (Figure 9-C-1d)** - used where switch is needed to control a lighting or appliance outlet and a receptacle that needs to remain constantly energized.

- **Switch and Pilot Light Combination (9-C-1e)** - used for special application installations where visible light is needed to indicate power is flowing through a switch (energized).

- **Double Switches (Figure 9-C-1f)** - used to control two outlets or appliances from the same switch location.

- **Rotary Dimmer Switch (Figure 9-C-1g)** - common style dimmer switch. Controls lighting intensity gradually from the "OFF " position to full brightness.

- **Slide Dimmer Switch (Figure 9-C-1h)** - popular dimmer style. Uses sliding lever to control lighting intensity.

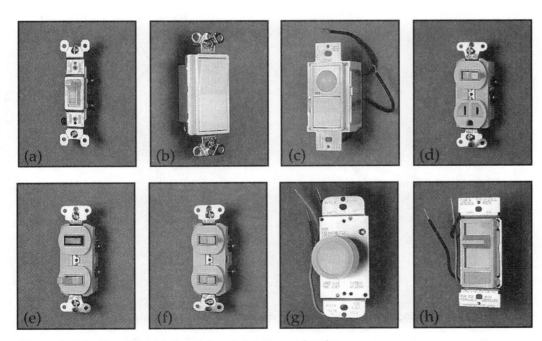

Figure 9-C-1. *Examples of common switch types and styles.*

D. Installing Single-Pole Switches

When installing switches, it is important that you recognize a distinct difference between the procedures for connecting receptacles and switches. Unlike receptacles, switches do not require the connection of a white grounded circuit conductor. Both conductors on a switch are considered "hot." This means that the white conductor, when used in a switch leg, acts as a hot conductor—not a grounded circuit conductor. When used in this fashion the white conductor must be identified as a hot conductor by wrapping it with a piece of electrical tape or some other means of permanent identification **(Figure 9-D-1)**.

■ The Switch Leg (Loop)

NEC® Reference
For more on
reidentification of
conductors, see
NEC® Article
200-7

It is common when connecting switches to the load (fixture or appliance) they control, for the power source to originate from an outlet box other than the switch device box. When this occurs, a connection called a **switch leg** (also called a **switch loop**) is needed to bring the power from the power source outlet to the switch **(Figure 9-D-1)**.

With this type of installation, the white conductor in the power source cable is connected to the input terminal on the switch. The **input (line)** terminal is considered the terminal located at the top of the switch. The remaining (bottom) terminal on the switch is called the **load** terminal.

The black conductor in the power source cable is connected to the load terminal on the switch and is responsible for delivering power to the brass (dark) terminal on the load.

Author's Note:
A white conductor
connected to a single
pole switch is always
called a "switch leg"
conductor.

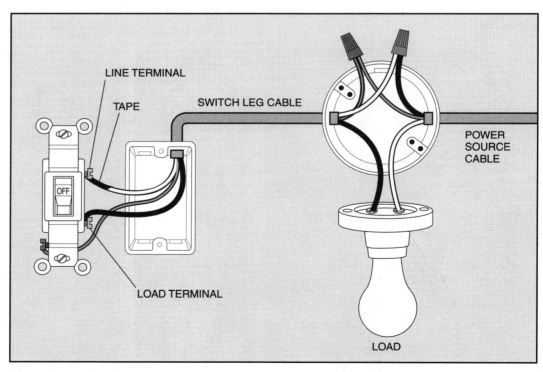

Figure 9-D-1. *An example of a single-pole switch leg (loop) installation.*

Installing a Single-Pole Switch to a Fixture with the Power Source Cable Entering at the Switch

In **Figure 9-D-2,** two (2) cables enter the switch box. The power source cable connects the switch to the overcurrent protection device in the SEP or subpanel. The remaining cable connects the switch to the lighting fixture.

① Lighting Fixture Connections

- Always begin the installation by connecting the **white** conductor to the **silver** screw terminal on the lighting fixture (load).

- Connect the **black** (hot) conductor to the **brass** screw terminal on the lighting fixture.

- Because the installation is made using a nonmetallic outlet box, fold the grounding conductor into the outlet box. **Do not remove.**

② Switch Connections

- Connect the **black** (hot) conductor in the power source cable to the **top** terminal on the switch.

  Connect the **black** (hot) conductor in the cable from the lighting outlet to the **bottom** terminal on the switch.

- Using a wire nut, connect the **white** conductors from both cables.

- Using a pigtail, connect all grounding conductors to the grounding terminal on the switch.

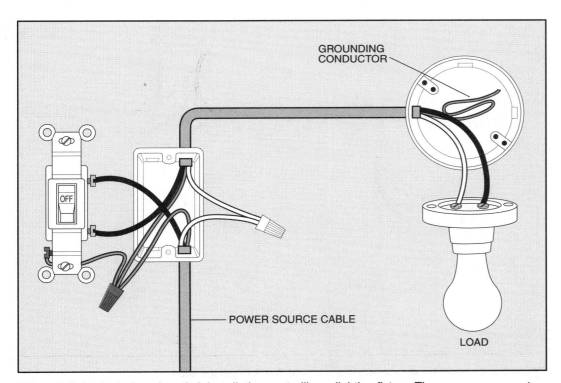

Figure 9-D-2. *A single-pole switch installation controlling a lighting fixture. The power source enters at the switch outlet.*

■ Installing a Single-Pole Switch to a Lighting Outlet With the Power Source Cable Entering at the Lighting Outlet

With this installation, the power source cable enters the lighting outlet box. Power is then sent to the switch through the switch leg cable **(Figure 9-D-3)**:

① Fixture Connections

- Connect the **white** conductor from the power source cable to the **silver** screw terminal on the fixture.

- Connect the **black** (hot) conductor from the switch leg to the brass screw terminal on the fixture.

- Using a wire nut, connect the **white** conductor from the switch cable to the **black** conductor from the power source cable.

- Connect the grounding conductors from the switch cable and the power cable.

② Switch Connections

- Connect the **white** conductor to the top terminal on the switch. Although not required, the author recommends that the white conductor be permanently identified with a black electrical tape.

- Connect the **black** conductor to the other terminal on the switch.

- Connect the grounding conductor to the **grounding** terminal.

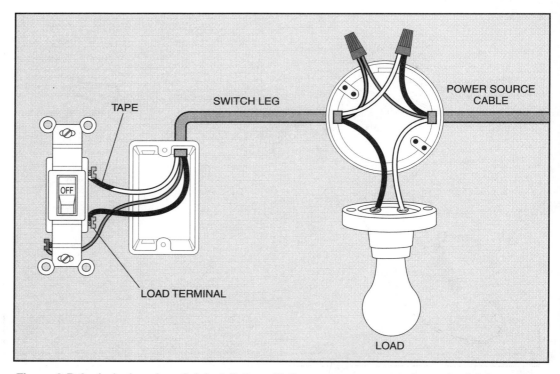

Figure 9-D-3. *A single-pole switch installation with the power source entering at the lighting outlet.*

Installing a Single-Pole Switch to (2) Lighting Outlets With the Power Source Entering at the Lighting Outlet

① Fixture #1 Connections (Figure 9-D-4)

- Using a **white pigtail jumper,** connect the **white** conductor from the power source cable and the **white** conductor from the cable serving lighting outlet #2 to the **silver** terminal on fixture #1.

- Connect the **black** conductor from the power source cable to the **white** conductor in the switch leg cable.

- Using a **black** pigtail jumper, connect the **black**conductors from the switch leg cable and the cable serving outlet #2 to the **brass** terminal on fixture #1.

- Connect the **grounding** conductor from the power source cable to the grounding conductor in the switch leg cable.

Fixture #2 Connections

- Connect the **white** conductor to the **silver** terminal and the **black** conductor to the brass terminal.

③ Switch Connections

- Make connections as shown.

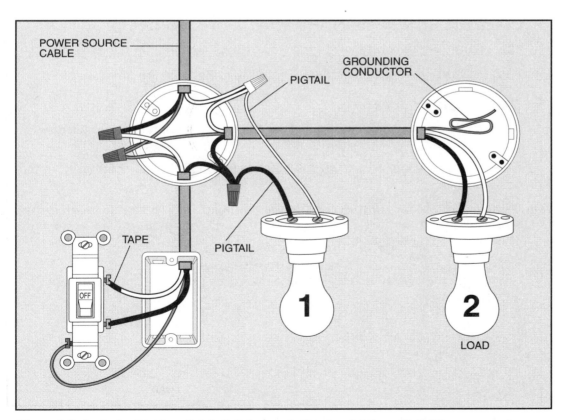

Figure 9-D-4. *A single-pole switch installation controlling two lighting outlets. The power source enters at the first lighting outlet.*

■ Installing (2) Single-Pole Switches to (2) Lighting Outlets With the Power Source Entering at the Lighting Outlet

In this installation, the power source cable enters at fixture outlet box #1. A threeconductor with ground cable is required as the switch leg between the two switches and lighting outlet #1. A two-conductor with ground cable is used for the cable between fixture #1 and fixture #2 **(Figure 9-D-5)**.

① Fixture #1 Connections

- Using a **white jumper** conductor (pigtail) and wire nut, connect the **white** conductors from the power source cable and the cable serving fixture outlet #2 to the **silver** terminal on fixture #1.

- Using a wire nut, connect the **black** conductor in the switch leg cable to the **black** conductor in the cable serving fixture outlet #2.

- Connect the **black** conductor from the power source cable to the **white** conductor in the switch leg cable serving the switch outlet boxes.

- Connect the **red** conductor in the switch leg cable to the **brass** terminal on the fixture.

- Using a wire nut, connect the grounding conductors from all three cables in the outlet box.

② Fixture #2 Connections

- Connect the **white** conductor to the **silver** screw terminal on the fixture.

- Connect the **black** conductor to the **brass** screw terminal on the fixture.

- Fold the cable grounding conductor into the outlet box. **Do Not Remove.**

③ Switch Connections

- Connect the **red** conductor from the switch leg cable to the bottom terminal on switch #1.

- Connect the **black** conductor from the switch leg cable to the bottom terminal on switch #2.

- Using two (2) **black jumper** conductors (pigtails) and a wire nut, connect the **white** conductor in the switch leg cable to the remaining terminals at the top of switch #1 and switch #2.

- Using two jumper conductors and a wire nut, connect the grounding conductor from the switch leg cable to the **green** grounding screw terminals on both switches.

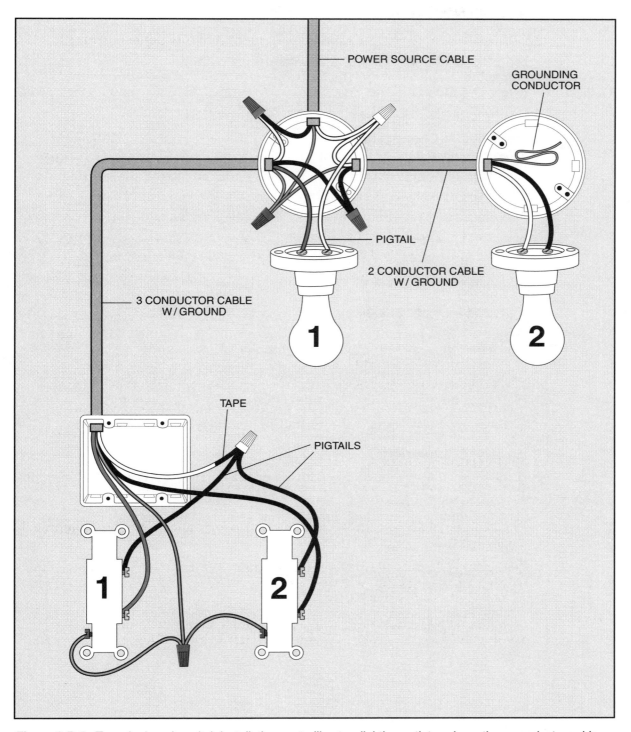

POWER SOURCE CABLE

GROUNDING
CONDUCTOR

PIGTAIL

2 CONDUCTOR CABLE
W / GROUND

3 CONDUCTOR CABLE
W / GROUND

1

2

TAPE

PIGTAILS

1

2

Figure 9-D-5. *Two, single-pole switch installation controlling two lighting outlets using a three conductor cable with ground. The power source enters at the first lighting outlet.*

■ Installing a Single-Pole Switch to (2) Lighting Outlets and an Unswitched Circuit

In residential wiring systems, circuits continue from outlet to outlet. To continue an unswitched circuit beyond switched light fixtures, a three-conductor with ground cable is required to connect the switch to the first and subsequent lighting fixtures on the circuit. A two-conductor with ground cable is used to continue the circuit as an unswitched power source serving additional loads. **Figure 9-D-6** illustrates these connection procedures. In this example, the power source cable enters the switch device outlet box.

❶ Fixture #1 Connections

- Using a **white** jumper conductor (pigtail) and wire nut, connect the **white** conductors from both cables entering the outlet box to the **silver** terminal on the fixture.

- Connect the **black** conductors from both cables with a wire nut.

- Using a **black (or red) jumper** conductor and wire nut, connect the **red** conductors from both cables to the brass terminal on the fixture.

- Using a wire nut, connect the grounding conductors from both cables.

❷ Fixture #2 Connections

- Using a **white jumper** conductor and wire nut, connect the **white** conductors from both cables to the **silver** screw terminal on the fixture.

- Connect the **red** conductor to the **brass** screw terminal on the lighting fixture.

- Connect the **black** conductors from both cables using a wire nut.

- Using a wire nut, connect the grounding conductors from both cables.

❸ Switch Connections

- Using a wire nut, connect the **white** conductors from both cables entering the device box.

- Using a wire nut and **black jumper** conductor (pigtail), connect the **black** conductors from the power source cable and the three-wire cable to the top terminal on the switch.

- Connect the **red** conductor in the connecting cable to the remaining lower terminal on the switch.

- Using a wire nut and jumper conductor, connect the grounding conductors from both cables to the **green** grounding screw terminal on the switch.

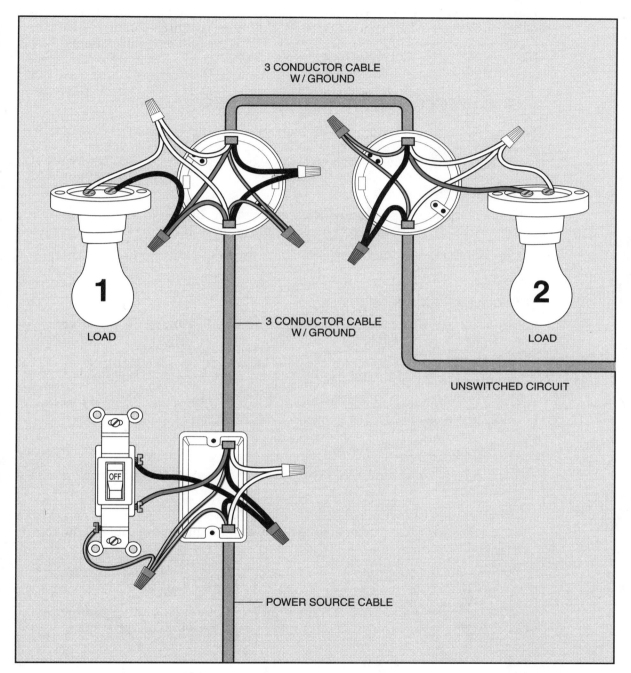

3 CONDUCTOR CABLE
W / GROUND

1

LOAD

3 CONDUCTOR CABLE
W / GROUND

2

LOAD

UNSWITCHED CIRCUIT

OFF

POWER SOURCE CABLE

Figure 9-D-6. *A single-pole switch controlling two lighting outlets. The circuit continues beyond the last lighting out and remains energized. It is not controlled by the switch.*

E. Installing Switched, Duplex Receptacles

Switched duplex receptacles are often used in the living areas of the home. where items such as lamps are used as the primary lighting source for a room. This type of switch allows the lamps to be controlled at a wall switch location. It can be installed to control one or both outlets on the receptacle.

■ Installing a Switched Duplex Receptacle

Author's Note:
Whenever possible, always connect the white conductor from the source cable to the top terminal on the switch.

The connections for a switched-duplex receptacle with the power source cable entering the receptacle outlet box is shown in **Figure 9-E-1**. The type of connection requires a two-conductor with ground cable.

① Switch Connections

- Connect the **white** conductor in the switch leg cable to the top terminal on the switch and the **black** conductor to the bottom terminal on the switch.

- Connect the grounding conductor to the **green** grounding screw on the switch.

② Receptacle Connections

- Connect the **white** conductor in the power source cable to the top **silver** terminal on the receptacle.

- Connect the **white** conductor from the switch leg cable to the **black** conductor in the power source cable.

- Using a pigtail jumper, connect the grounding conductors from each of the cables to the grounding terminal on the receptacle.

Author's Note:
The white conductor in the power source cable must be connected to the silver terminal on the receptacle. It functions as the grounded circuit conductor.

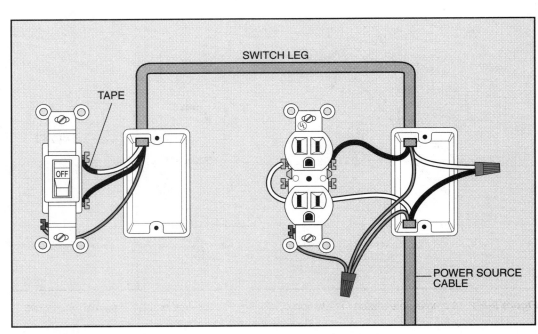

Figure 9-E-1. *A single-pole switch Installation controlling a switched duplex receptacle. The power source enters at the receptacle outlet.*

Installing a Switched, Split-Duplex Receptacle

It is often desirable to have one-half of a receptacle controlled by a switch and the other half of the switch to remain constantly hot. The procedures for this type of installation are shown in **Figure 9-E-2** using two-conductor cable with ground.

① Preparing the receptacle

- Select the outlet (top or bottom) on the receptacle you wish to connect to the switch and remove the tab between the brass terminals on the receptacle. (For illustrative purposes, the top outlet of the switch shown below has been selected).

② Making the receptacle connections

- Connect the **black** conductor from the switch leg cable to the top brass terminal on the receptacle.

- Using a **white** jumper conductor (pigtail), connect the **white** conductors from the power source cable and the cable to the next receptacle to one of the **silver** terminals on the receptacle.

- Using a **black** jumper conductor (pigtail), connect the **white** conductor from the switch leg cable and the **black** conductors from the power source cable and the cable to the next receptacle, to the bottom **brass** terminal on the receptacle.

- Using a pigtail jumper, connect the grounding conductors in each cable to the grounding screw terminal on the receptacle.

③ Make the normal connections to the single-pole switch

Author's Note:
To create a split-duplex receptacle, you must remove one of the connecting tabs between the outlets.

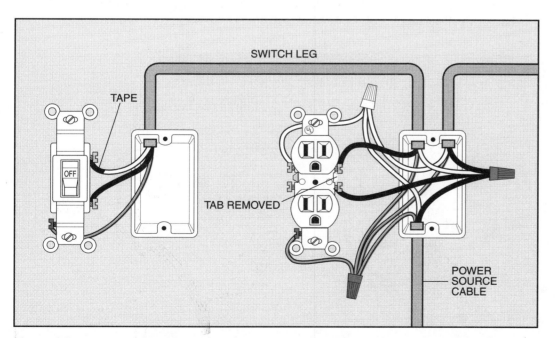

Figure 9-E-2. *A single-pole switch installation controlling the top half of a split-duplex receptacle.*

F. Installing Switched-Combination Receptacles

Combination receptacles are often used to provide lighting in small areas where limited receptacle access is needed. Combination receptacles are equipped with three brass terminals and only one silver terminal.

The combination switch/receptacle shown below in **(Figure 9-F-1)** illustrates the switch portion of the receptacle controlling a lighting fixture while the outlet portion of the receptacle remains hot.

① Fixture Connections

- Connect the **white** conductor in the lighting outlet cable to the **silver** terminal on the fixture and the **black** conductor to the **brass** terminal on the fixture.

- Fold the cable grounding conductor into the outlet box. **Do not remove.**

② Switch Connections

- Using a **white jumper** conductor and a wire nut, connect the white conductors from the power source cable and the lighting outlet cable to the **silver** terminal on the receptacle.

- Using (2) **black jumper** conductors (pigtails) and a wire nut, connect the **black** conductor from the power source cable to both **brass** terminals on the switch.

- Connect the **black** conductor from the lighting outlet cable to the remaining **brass** terminal located above the **silver** terminal.

- Using a pigtail jumper, connect the grounding conductors from both cables to the grounding terminal.

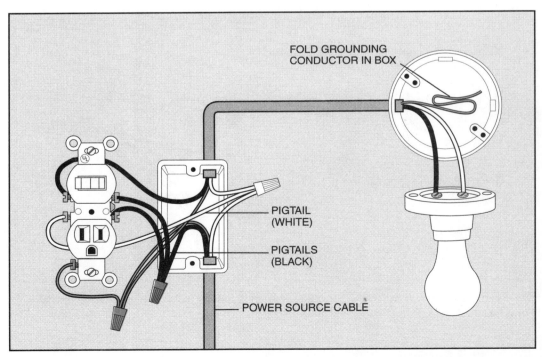

Figure 9-F-1. *A combination switch/receptacle installation controlling a lighting fixture. The power source enters at the switch.*

G. Installing Double-Pole Switches

This type of installation used when it is necessary to install a switch controlling a piece of large equipment requiring 240-volt service. The installation requires a, double-pole switch and a receptacle rated for 240-volts **(Figure 9-G-1)**. The double-pole switch is equipped with (4) four brass terminals and a green grounding terminal. The receptacle is equipped with specially configured contact slots.

① Connecting the Double-Pole Switch

- Connect the **white** conductors in the power source cable and the receptacle cable to the terminals on one side of the switch. Identify each with black tape as an ungrounded, energized conductor.

- Connect the **black** conductors in the power source cable and the receptacle cable to the corresponding terminals on the opposite side of the switch.

- Using a jumper conductor and wire nut, connect the grounding conductors from both cables to the **green** grounding screw terminal on the switch.

② Connecting the 240-volt Receptacle

- Connect the **white** conductor in the receptacle cable to one of the top terminals on the receptacle.

- Connect the **black** conductor in the receptacle cable to the top terminal on the opposite side of the receptacle.

- Connect the grounding conductor to the grounding terminal.

NEC® Reference
For more on conductor reidentification, seeNEC® Article 200-7

Author's Note:
In this installation, the white conductor in the power source cable is not a grounded circuit conductor. It is an energized conductor and must be re-identified as such.

NOTE: RE-IDENTIFICATION OF WHITE CONDUCTORS IS REQUIRED

TAPE

OFF

TAPE

240-VOLT DUPLEX RECEPTACLE

POWER SOURCE CABLE

Figure 9-G-1. A double-pole switch installation controlling a 240-volt duplex receptacle. The power source enters at the switch.

H. Installing Dimmer Switches

Dimmer switches are commonly used in today's modern home lighting systems. They are most often used in bedrooms, dining room, dens and other areas where the homeowner desires to vary the brightness of the area lighting.

They are sometimes slightly larger than a typical switch but will easily fit into a standard device box. Because of the heat they generate, they should not be installed in device boxes that are filled with other circuit conductors or in undersized device boxes.

Author's Note:
When connecting a device with color coded conductors, always make the circuit conductor connections to like colors on the device; white-to- white , black-to- black, etc.

Dimmer switches also differ from common switches in that they do not have screw terminals. They are manufactured with their conductors already installed. Depending on the manufacturer, they may come with or without a green grounding conductor. If you select a dimmer switch equipped with a green grounding screw, it must connected to the cable grounding conductor. **Figures 9-H-1** and **9-H-2** show dimmer switches equipped with and without a grounding conductor.

- Connect one of the conductors from the switch to one of the power source cable conductors. The conductors on the switch are interchangeable and can be connected to either of the cable conductors.

- If equipped with an equipment grounding conductor, connect it to the cable grounding conductor with a wire nut **(Figure 9-H-1)**.

- Connect the remaining conductors on the switch. If the switch is not equipped with an equipment grounding conductor, simply fold the cable grounding conductor into the box for future use **(Figure 9-H-2)**.

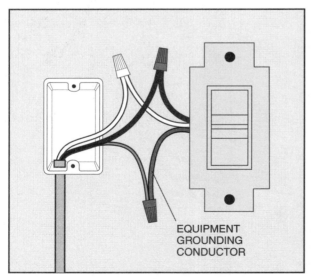

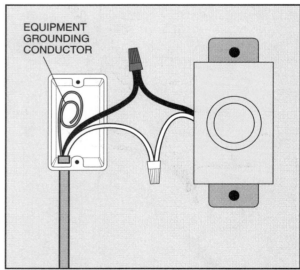

Figure 9-H-1. A slide type dimmer switch installation. The grounding conductor is manufactured into the switch and must be connected to the grounding conductor in the power source cable.

Figure 9-H-2. A rotary type dimmer switch installation. If the switch has no equipment grounding conductor, the power source grounding conductor should be folded into the box for future use.

I. Installing Ceiling Fan Switches

Ceiling fan installations are common in today's modern residences. They are often installed in bedrooms, family rooms, dining rooms, bathrooms or anywhere the homeowner feels the desire for the extra comfort of a cooling breeze. Wiring connections for a typical fan installation can easily be accomplished by using the manufacturer's directions for fan installation.

Most fan/lighting installations will require a special fan rated outlet box. A typical outlet box used for common outlets will not withstand the fan movement and constant vibration. Many injuries have been caused by not using the proper box and box installation procedures. Be sure to select a fan box rated for the equipment you are to install.

NEC® References
For more on ceiling fan installations, seeNEC® Articles
370-23
370-27
422-18

Figure 9-I-1 below illustrates the fan connections for the overhead fan/light combination in bedroom #1 on the sample house plan.Connection requires two, single-pole switches. Switch #1 controls the fan portion of the fixture; switch #2 controls the light portion.

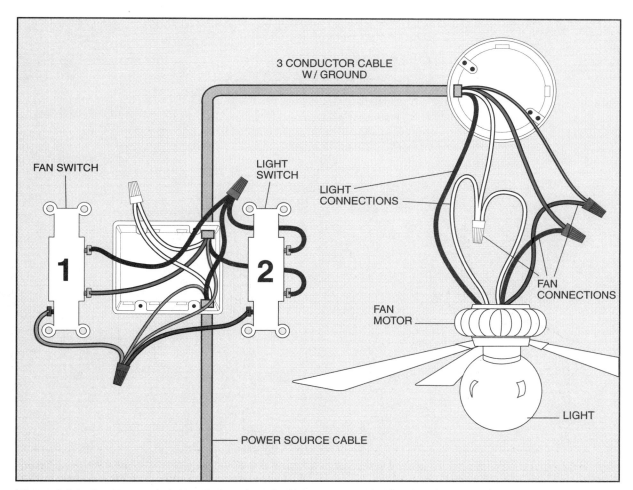

Figure 9-I-1. *Separate switch installations for a fan/light combination. Switch #1 controls the fan. Switch #2 controls the lighting fixture .*

Notes

Three & Four-Way Switches

Three and four-way switches make it convenient to control lighting from multiple locations in large rooms, long hallways, stairways and between the residence and outside utility building or garages **(Figures 10-1 and 10-2)**. The use of three and four-way switches is common in most modern homes and can be easily installed armed with the right information.

In this chapter you will learn how to successfully install three and four-way switches in a variety of circuit installation options. Each type of switch is discussed under:

A. Three-Way Switches

B. Four-Way Switches

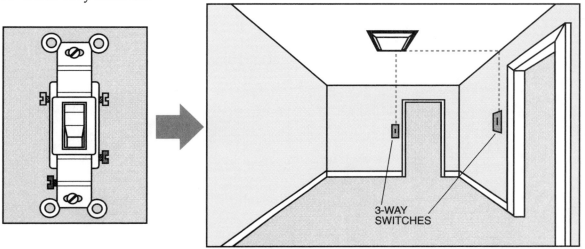

Figure 10-1. *Three-way switches permit lighting controls from two locations.*

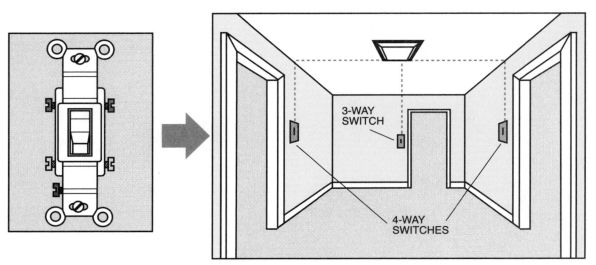

Figure 10-2. *Four-way switches permit lighting controls from three or more locations.*

A. Three-Way Switches

Why are three-way switches called "three-way switches?" ***Three-way*** refers to the number of terminals on the switch (**Figure 10-A-1**)—not the number of switch locations. There are four (4) important factors that will help you recognize and properly install three-way switches:

(1) Three-way switches are equipped with three terminals: (two) brass terminals called **"traveler terminals"** located on opposite sides of the switch and (one) dark-colored screw terminal called the **"common terminal."** On most switches, the word **common** may be printed next to the terminal. The common terminal may also be called a **"hinge."** It is important to remember that the location of the common terminal on the switch may differ depending on the manufacturer. The common terminal is always identified by its darker color or by the manufacturer's installation directions. Three-way switches, like most of today's modern switch and receptacle installations, come equipped with green grounding screw terminals.

(2) A three-way switch has no "ON-OFF" marking on the switch toggle. Technically, there is no top or bottom to the three- way switch; no "up" or "down."The common terminal on the switch in **Figure 10-A-1** is shown on the lower right portion of the switch. However, it could also be installed with the common terminal in the upper left portion of the switch and still function properly so long as it is identified as the common terminal.

(3) Three-way switches must always be installed in pairs.

(4) Three-way switches must always use three-conductor with ground cable between switches.

Author's Note:
Always read the manufacturer's directions before installing any electrical device.

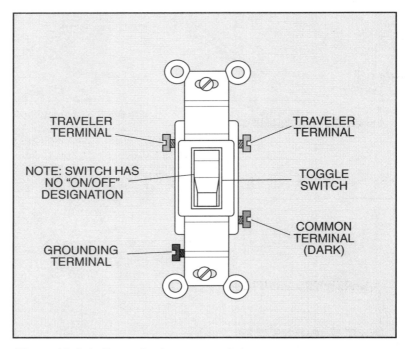

Figure 10-A-1. *Parts of a three-way switch.*

How Three-Way Switches Work

A common question usually asked about three-way switches is, "How does a three-way switch work?" **Figure 10-A-2** below illustrates the principle for how a three-way works.

A three-way switch consists of three internal contacts: two (2) traveler terminals and one (1) common terminal **(Figure 10-A-2a)**. When the switch toggle moves to the "DOWN" position, the contacts are made to one of the traveler terminals **(Figure 10 -A-2b)**. When moved in the "UP" position, the contacts are made to the opposite traveler terminal **(Figure 10-A-2c)**. This means there is always a pair of "made" contacts in a three-way switch. This allows the lighting fixture to be turned"OFF" or "ON" at either of the switch locations.

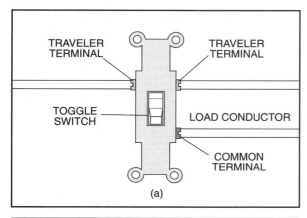

Figure 10-A-2a. Three-way switches are equipped with two traveler terminals and one common terminal.

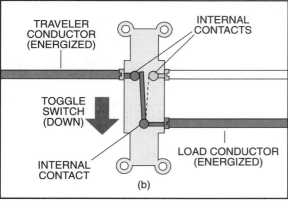

Figure 10-A-2b. When the switch toggle is moved to a down or up position, the switch energizes the circuit to the load by connecting one set of the internal contacts.

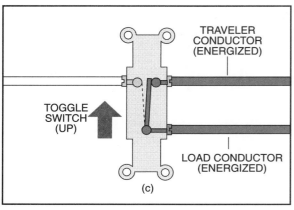

Figure 10-A-2c. When the switch toggle is moved in the opposite position (up or down), the second set of contacts are energized.

■ Steps for Installing a Three-Way Switched Circuit

To beginners— and sometimes, even to experienced electricians—installing a three-way switch circuit can be a confusing process. However, learning a few simple rules will help makes the installation go smoothly.

Figure 10-A-3 illustrates an example of a simple step-by-step method for installing a three-way switched circuit.

NOTE: This and subsequent illustrations may be shown without device boxes and grounding conductors. Detailed procedures illustrating the use of each and their specific installations are shown later in this section.

Installing three-way switches will require a three-conductor cable with ground. A two-conductor cable with ground is required from the power source.

① Lighting Fixture (Load) Connections

- Connect the **white** conductor in cable #1 to the **silver** screw terminal on the lighting fixture (load).

- Connect the **black** conductor in cable #2 to the **brass** screw terminal on the load (lighting fixture).

- Using a wire nut, connect the **black** conductor in cable #1 to the **white** conductor in cable #2.

- Using a wire nut, connect the **red** conductors in cable #1 and cable #2 .

② Switch #1 Connections

- Connect the **white** conductor in the power source cable to the **white** conductor in the lighting fixture connecting cable.

- Connect the **black** conductor in the power source cable to the **common** (dark) terminal on switch #1.

- Connect the **red** conductor in cable #1 to one of the terminals on switch #1.

- Connect the remaining **black** conductor in cable #1 to the remaining terminal on switch #1.

③ Switch #2 Connections

- Connect the **black** conductor in cable #2 to the **common** (dark) terminal on switch #2.

- Connect the **white** and **red** conductors in cable #2 to the remaining light colored terminals on the switch.

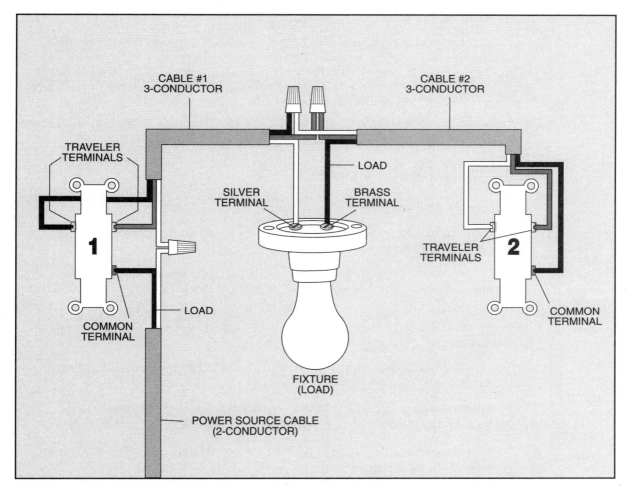

Figure 10-A-3. *A basic wiring layout for a three-way switched circuit.*

■ Installing a Three-Way Switched Circuit With the Power Source Originating at the Lighting Outlet

The steps shown in **Figure 10-A-4** are illustrated using nonmetallic boxes. The power source cable enters the lighting fixture outlet box.

① Lighting Fixture (Load) Connections

- Connect the **white** conductor in the power source cable to the **silver** screw terminal on the lighting fixture (load).

- Using a wire nut, connect the **black** (traveler) conductor in the power source cable to the **white** conductor in cable #1.

- Connect the **black** (traveler) conductor in cable #1 to the **brass** screw terminal on the lighting fixture.

- Using a wire nut, connect the grounding conductors in the power source cable and cable #1.

② Switch #1 Connections

- Connect the **black** (traveler) conductor in cable #1 to the **common** (dark) terminal on the switch.

- Using a wire nut, connect the **white** conductor in cable #1 to the **white** conductor in cable #2. Identify these as **hot** conductors using black electrical tape.

- Connect the **red** (traveler) conductor in cable #2 to either of the terminals on switch #1.

- Connect the **black** (traveler) conductor in cable #2 to the remaining terminal on switch #1.

- Using a wire nut and pigtail jumper conductor, connect the grounding conductors in cables #1 and #2 to the **green** grounding screw terminal on the switch.

③ Switch #2 Connections

- Connect the **white** conductor in cable #2 to the **common** (dark) terminal on the switch.

- Connect the **red** and **black** (traveler) conductors in cable #2 to the remaining terminals on the switch.

- Connect the grounding conductor to the **green** grounding screw terminal on the switch.

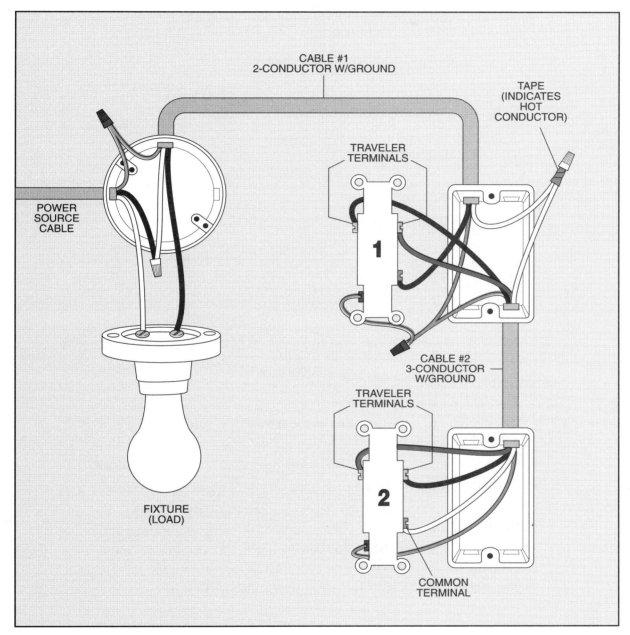

Figure 10-A-4. *A three-way switched lighting circuit with the power source entering at the lighting outlet.*

■ Installing a Three-Way Switched Circuit With the Power Source Originating at the First Switch Outlet

The steps shown in **Figure 10-A-5** are illustrated using nonmetallic boxes. The power source cable enters the device box at switch #1.

① Lighting Fixture (Load) Connections

- Connect the **white** conductor in cable #2 to the **silver** screw terminal on the lighting fixture.

- Connect the **black** conductor in cable #2 to the **brass** screw terminal on the lighting fixture.

- Fold the grounding conductor into the outlet box. **Do Not Remove.**

② Switch #1 Connections

- Connect the **black** conductor in the power source cable to the **common** (dark) terminal on switch #1.

- Using a wire nut, connect the **white** conductor from the power source cable to the **white** conductor cable #1.

- Connect the **black** and **red** conductors (travelers) in cable #1 to the terminals on switch #1.

- Using a wire nut and pigtail jumper conductor, connect the grounding conductors from the power source cable and cable #1 to the **green** grounding screw terminal on the switch.

③ Switch #2 Connections

- Connect the **black** conductor in cable #2 to the **common** (dark) terminal on switch #2.

- Using a wire nut, connect the **white** conductors in cables #1 and #2.

- Connect the **red** conductor (traveler) in cable #1 to one of the light colored terminals on switch #2.

- Connect the **black** conductor in cable #1 serving the lighting outlet (load) to the remaining light colored terminal on the switch.

- Using a wire nut and jumper conductor, connect all grounding conductors to the **green** grounding screw terminal on the switch.

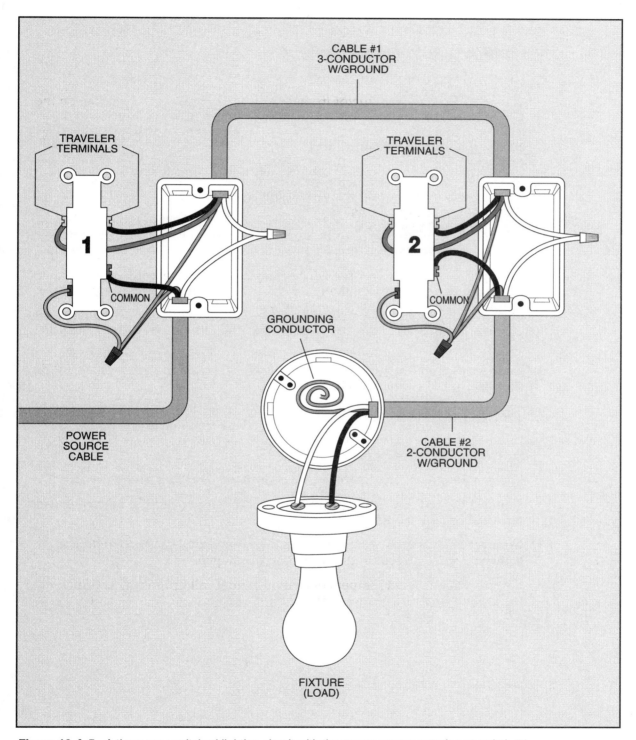

CABLE #1
3-CONDUCTOR
W/GROUND

TRAVELER
TERMINALS

TRAVELER
TERMINALS

1

2

COMMON

COMMON

GROUNDING
CONDUCTOR

POWER
SOURCE
CABLE

CABLE #2
2-CONDUCTOR
W/GROUND

FIXTURE
(LOAD)

Figure 10-A-5. *A three-way switched lighting circuit with the power source entering at switch #1.*

■ Installing a Three-Way Switched Circuit With the Lighting Outlet Between Switches

The steps shown in **Figure 10-A-6** are illustrated using nonmetallic boxes. The power source cable enters the device box at switch #1.

① Lighting Fixture (Load) Connections

- Connect the **white** conductor from cable #1 to the **silver** screw terminal on the lighting fixture.

- Connect the **black** conductor from cable #1 to the **white** conductor in cable #2. The **white** conductor in cable #2 is used as part of a switch loop (leg) and does not require re-identification.

- Connect the **red** conductor in cable #1 to the **red** conductor in cable #2.

- Using a wire nut, connect the grounding conductors in cables #1 and #2.

② Switch #1 Connections

- Connect the **black** conductor from the power source cable to the **common** (dark) terminal on switch #1.

- Using a wire nut, connect the **white** conductor from the power source cable to the **white** conductor in cable #1.

- Connect the **black** conductor in cable #1 to one of the traveler terminals on the switch.

- Connect the **red** conductor in cable #1 to the remaining traveler terminal on the switch.

- Using a wire nut and jumper conductor, connect the grounding conductors from both cables to the **green** grounding screw terminal on switch #1.

③ Switch #2 Connections

- Connect the **black** conductor to the **common** (dark) terminal on switch #2.

- Connect the **red** and **white** conductors to the remaining light colored traveler terminals on the switch.

- Connect the grounding conductor to the **green** grounding screw on the switch.

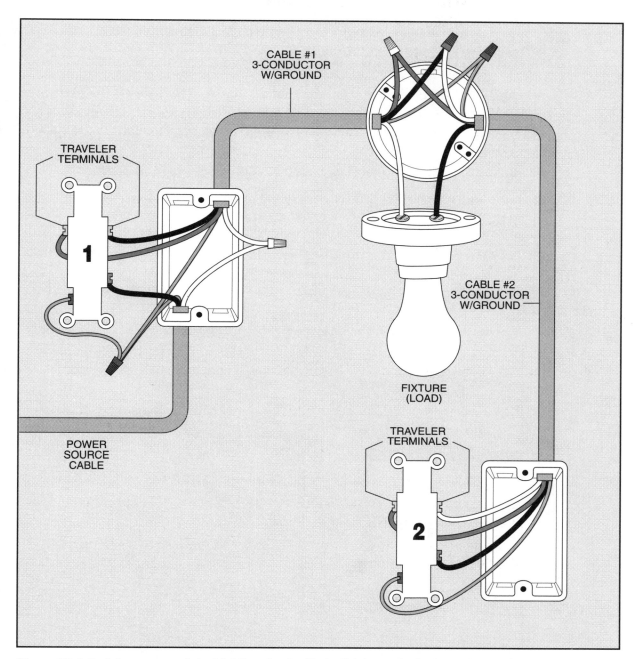

CABLE #1
3-CONDUCTOR
W/GROUND

TRAVELER
TERMINALS

1

POWER
SOURCE
CABLE

CABLE #2
3-CONDUCTOR
W/GROUND

FIXTURE
(LOAD)

TRAVELER
TERMINALS

2

Figure 10-A-6. *A three-way switched lighting circuit with the lighting outlet between the switches. The power source enters at switch #1.*

B. Four-Way Switches

Four-way switches receive their name, as does the three-way switch, from the number of terminals on the switch—not the number of switch installations on the circuit. Four-way switches are equipped with (2) sets of terminals, but have no common terminal. Some manufacturers will make a distinction between these two sets of terminals by color coding one set of terminals with a darker color. However, some manufacturers make no color distinction. It is the responsibility of the electrical installer to read the instructions supplied with the switch to determine how to properly install the switch. **Figure 10-B-1** shows the parts of a four-way switch.

Below are some basic rules you must be aware of when considering installing four-way switch circuits:

(1) Four-way switches can be used only in combination with three-way switches.

(2) Four-way switches are always installed <u>between</u> (2) three-way switches. You may install as many four-way switches as is necessary—but they must always be located between three-way switches.

(3) Four-way switches, like three-way switches, have no top or bottom designation. The switch toggle has no "On/Off" markings.

(4) Four -way switches have no common terminal as do three-way switches.

Author's Note:
The physical orientation of the switch will determine how the contacts will be connected. Always look for the difference in terminal colors before making connections.

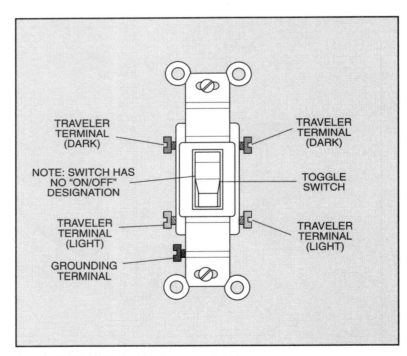

Figure 10-B-1. *Parts of a four-way switch.*

Four-Way Switches and How They Work

Like single-pole and three-way switches, four-way switches perform their special functions through the arrangement of their internal contact terminals.

One important piece of information that you will need to learn and remember about four-way switches is the following:

In four-way switches there always exists (2) pairs of made contacts. One set of contacts is made either in a **vertical** or **horizontal configuration** (depending on the type of switch being used) when the toggle on the switch is moved in one direction. When the toggle switch is moved in the opposite direction, the contacts for both the vertical and horizontal switches are made diagonally.

Four way switches are available in two different types. Each is based on the manufactured configuration of the terminal locations on each type of switch.

(1) Vertically configured terminals

(2) Horizontally configured terminals

In a four-way switch with vertically configured terminals, the terminals, usually darker in color, are located on opposite sides of the switch **(Figure 10-B-2)**.

In a four-way switch with horizontally configured terminals, the darker terminals are located on the same side of the switch **(Figure 10-B-3)**.

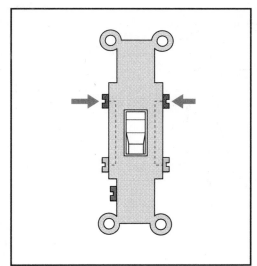

Figure 10-B-2 A four-way switch with vertically configured terminals.

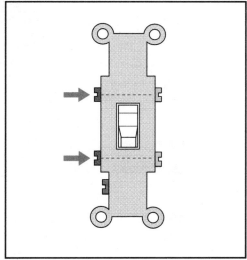

Figure 10-B-3. A four-way switch with horizontally configured terminals.

NOTE: Today, most four-way switches have a vertical terminal configuration. However, some switch manufacturers also produce switches with a horizontal terminal configuration. You must decide which type switch you have by checking the color and location of the terminals on the switch and by reading the manufacturer's installation directions.

▼ Four-Way Switch (Vertically Configured Terminals)

A vertically configured 4-way switch can be identified by the two darker terminals located on opposite sides of the switch. The hot conductors in traveler cable #1 (serving three-way switch #1) are connected to the two, darker colored terminals at the top and on either side of the switch **(Figure 10-B-4a)**. The hot conductors in the traveler cable #2 (serving three-way switch #2) are connected to the two traveler terminals opposite each other at the bottom of the 4-way switch **(Figure 10-B-4b)**. When the switch toggle is moved to the "up" position, the connections are made to the "vertical" contacts in the switch. When the switch toggle is moved to the "down" position, the connections are made to the contacts "diagonally" across the switch.

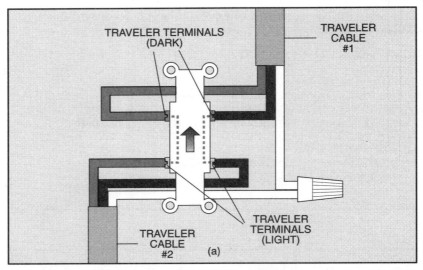

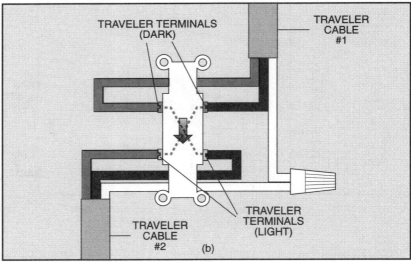

Figure 10-B-4. *(a) Internal contacts are made vertically when the switch toggle is moved to an up or down position. (b) Internal contacts are made diagonally when the switch toggle is moved in the opposite position (up or down).*

Simple Steps for Installing a Vertically Configured, Four-Way Switched Circuit

For illustrative purposes, the grounding conductors and switch grounding terminals are omitted in the basic wiring layout shown in **Figure 10-B-5.**

① Three-Way Switch #1 Connections

- Make the connections to the **common** terminal and to the traveler terminals as shown.

- Using a wire nut, connect the **white** conductor in the power source cable to the **white** conductor in traveler cable #1 using a wire nut.

② Four-Way Switch Connections

- Connect the **red** and **black** (traveler) conductors from cable #1 to the dark terminals on the switch.

- Connect the **red** and **black** (traveler) conductors from cable #2 to the light colored terminals on the switch.

- Using a wire nut, connect the **white** conductor in cable #1 to the white conductor in cable #2 .

③ Three-Way Switch #2 Connections

- Make the connection to the **common** terminal and to the traveler terminals as shown.

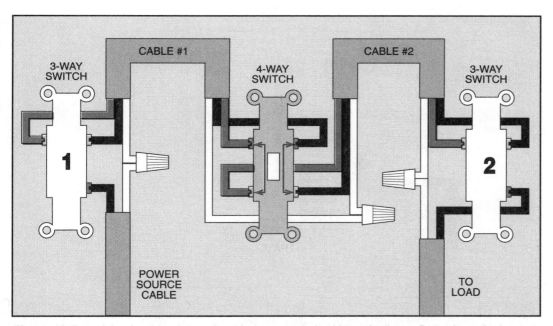

Figure 10-B-5. *A basic wiring layout for a four-way switch with vertically configured terminals.*

▼ Four-Way Switch (Horizontally Configured Terminals)

A 4-way switch with horizontally configured terminals can be identified by the (2) dark terminals located on the same side of the switch. The hot conductors in traveler cable #1 are connected to the dark traveler terminals located on the same side of the 4-way switch. The traveler conductors in traveler cable #2 are connected to the lighter colored traveler terminals located on the opposite side of the 4-way switch. When the switch toggle is moved to the "up" position, the contacts are made to the "horizontal" contacts in the switch **(Figure 10-B-6a)**. When the toggle handle is moved to the "down" position, the connections are made to the contacts "diagonally" across the switch **(Figure 10-B-6b).**

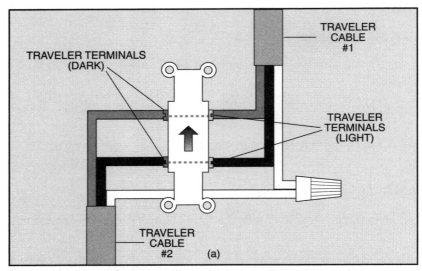

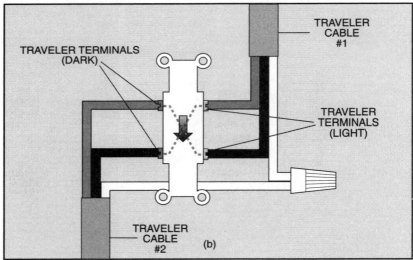

Figure 10-B-6. *(a) Internal contacts are made horizontally when the switch toggle is moved to the up or down position. (b) Internal contacts are made diagonally when the switch toggle is moved in the opposite position (up or down).*

■ Simple Steps for Installing a Horizontally Configured, Four-Way Switched Circuit

For illustrative purposes, the grounding conductors and the switch grounding terminals are omitted in the basic wiring layout shown in **Figure 10-B-7.**

① Three-Way Switch #1 Connections

- Make the connections to the **common** terminal and to the traveler terminals as shown.

- Using a wire nut, connect the **white** conductor from the power source cable to the **white** conductor in traveler cable #1.

② Four-Way Switch Connections

- Connect the **red** and **black** traveler conductors from traveler cable #1 to the dark terminals located on the side of the switch.

- Connect the **red** and black traveler conductors in cable #2 to the light colored terminals on the switch.

- Connect the **white** conductor in cable#1 to the **white** conductor in cable #2 using a wire nut.

③ Three-Way Switch #2 Connections

- Make the connections to the **common** terminal and to the traveler terminals as shown.

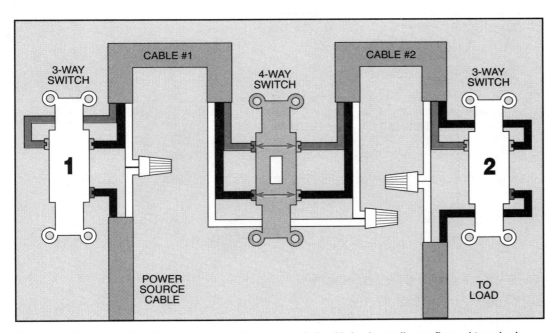

Figure 10-B-7. *A basic wiring layout for a four-way switch with horizontally configured terminals.*

■ Installing a Vertically Configured, Four-Way Switched Circuit

The steps shown in **Figure 10-B-8** are illustrated using nonmetallic boxes. The power source cable enters at the lighting outlet box.

❶ Lighting Fixture (Load) Connections

* Connect the **white** conductor from the power source cable to the **silver** screw terminal on the lighting fixture.

* Connect the **black** conductor in cable #1 to the **brass** screw terminal on the lighting fixture.

* Using a wire nut, connect the **black** conductor from the power source cable to the **white** conductor in cable #1.

* Using a wire nut, connect the grounding conductors from the power source cable and cable #1.

❷ 3-Way Switch #1 Connections

* Connect the **black** conductor in cable #1 to the **common** (dark) terminal on switch #1.

* Connect the **red** and **white** conductors in cable #2 to the traveler terminals on switch #1.

* Using a wire nut, connect the **white** conductor in cable #1 to the **black** conductor in cable #2.

* Using a jumper conductor (pigtail) and wire nut, connect the grounding conductors from both cables to the **green** grounding screw terminal on the switch.

❸ 4-Way Switch Connections

* Using a wire nut, connect the **black** conductor in cable #2 to the **black** conductor in cable #3.

* Connect the **red** and **white** conductors in cable #2 to the dark colored terminals at the top and on either side of the four-way switch.

* Connect the **red** and **white** conductors in cable #3 to the light colored terminals on the lower half of the switch.

* Using a jumper conductor (pigtail) and wire nut, connect the grounding conductors from cables #2 and #3 to the **green** grounding screw terminal on the switch.

❹ 3-Way Switch #2 Connections

* Connect the **black** conductor in cable #3 to the **common** (dark) terminal on switch #2.

* Connect the **red** and **white** conductors to the remaining traveler terminals on the switch.

* Connect the grounding conductor to the **green** grounding screw terminal on the switch.

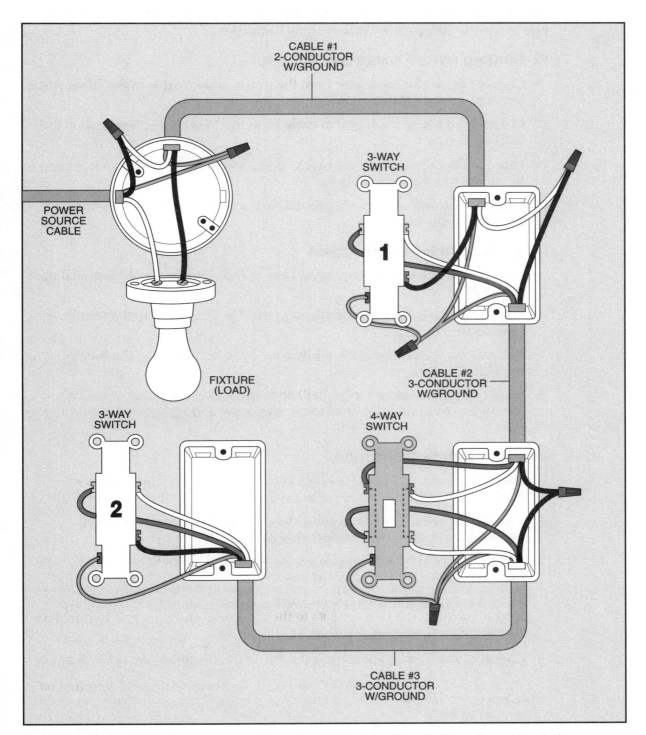

Figure 10-B-8. *A four-way switched circuit using a four-way switch with vertically configured terminals.*

■ Installing a Horizontally Configured, Four-Way Switched Circuit

The steps shown in **Figure 10-B-9** are illustrated using nonmetallic boxes. The power source cable enters at the lighting outlet box.

❶ Lighting Fixture (Load) Connections

* Connect the **white** conductor from the power source cable to the **silver** screw terminal on the lighting fixture.

* Connect the **black** conductor in cable #1 to the **brass** screw terminal on the lighting fixture.

* Using a wire nut, connect the **black** conductor from the power source cable to the **white** conductor in cable #1.

* Using a wire nut, connect the grounding conductors in the power source cable and cable #1.

❷ 3-Way Switch #1 Connections

* Connect the **black** conductor in cable #1 to the **common** (dark) terminal on switch #1.

* Using a wire nut, connect the **white** conductor in cable #1 to the **black** conductor in cable #2.

* Connect the **red** and **white** conductors in cable #2 to the traveler terminals on the switch.

* Using a jumper conductor (pigtail) and wire nut, connect the grounding conductors in cables #1 and #2 to the **green** grounding screw terminal on the switch.

❸ 4-Way Switch Connections

* Connect the **red** and **white** conductors in cable #2 to the dark colored terminals located on one side of the switch.

* Connect the **red** and **white** conductors in cable #3 to the light colored terminals located on the opposite side of the switch.

* Using a wire nut, connect the **black** conductors in cables #2 and #3.

* Using a jumper conductor and wire nut, connect the grounding conductors cables #2 and #3 to the **green** grounding screw terminal.

❹ 3-Way Switch #2 Connections

* Connect the **black** conductor in cable #3 to the **common** (dark) terminal on the switch.

* Connect the **red** and **white** conductors to the light colored traveler terminals on the switch.

* Connect the grounding conductor to the **green** grounding screw terminal on the switch.

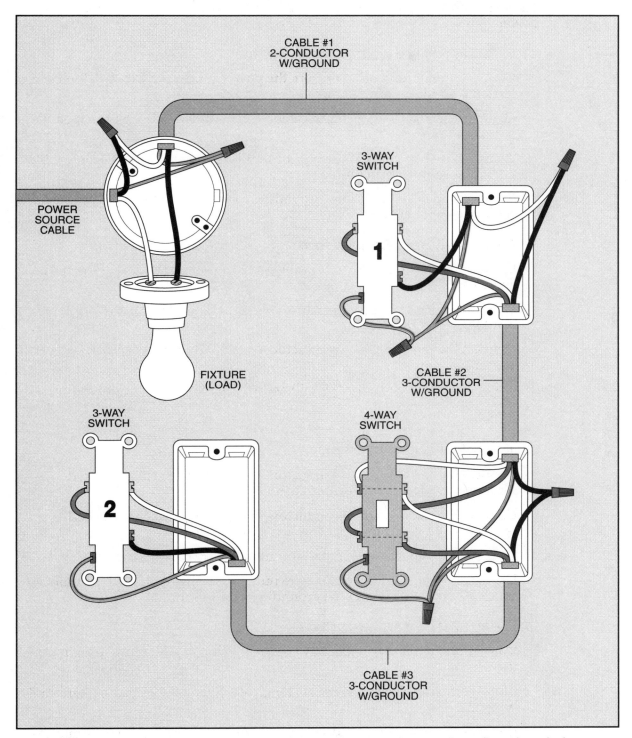

CABLE #1
2-CONDUCTOR
W/GROUND

POWER
SOURCE
CABLE

3-WAY
SWITCH

1

FIXTURE
(LOAD)

CABLE #2
3-CONDUCTOR
W/GROUND

3-WAY
SWITCH

2

4-WAY
SWITCH

CABLE #3
3-CONDUCTOR
W/GROUND

Figure 10-8-9. *A four-way switched circuit using a four-way switch with horizontally configured terminals.*

Notes

Service Entrance Panels & Subpanels

Earlier in this publication you learned that service entrance panels and subpanels function as the termination point for the branch circuits and the service entrance conductors. Electrical current arrives from the utility supplier and enters the residential wiring system at the service entrance panel. Electrical current is sent to all parts of the residence through a network of branch and feeder circuits. Each circuit is controlled and protected by its own overcurrent protection device (circuit breaker) located in the service entrance and/or subpanel **(Figure 11-1)**.

Service entrance panels and subpanels used in today's modern residential wiring installations come in various styles, sizes and designs depending on the manufacturer and need. Each type of panel and installation requirements is discussed under the topics:

A. Service Entrance Panels

B. Subpanels

C. Service Entrance Conductors

D. Selecting Service Entrance Panels and Subpanels

Figure 11-1. *All service entrance panels and subpanels must be installed to comply with NEC® and local code requirements. Here, an electrical inspector examines a service entrance panel .*

A. Service Entrance Panels

Service entrance panels, in every case, provide the first means of disconnect from the service utility to the residential wiring system. They also include overcurrent protection for the branch and feeder circuits that make up the wiring system. They may be located either inside or outside the residence near a point where the service entrance conductors enter the residence. The number of circuit breaker positions may vary from as few to a permitted maximum of 42. No service entrance panel may contain more than 42 overcurrent protection device positions.

Service entrance panels, depending on their requirements and manufacturer, may differ in size, shape and design, but their function is always the same.

Figure 11-A-1 illustrates the basic parts of a service entrance panel. Descriptions for each part are shown on page 179.

NEC® Reference
For more on Service Entrance Panels, see NEC® Article 230-70a

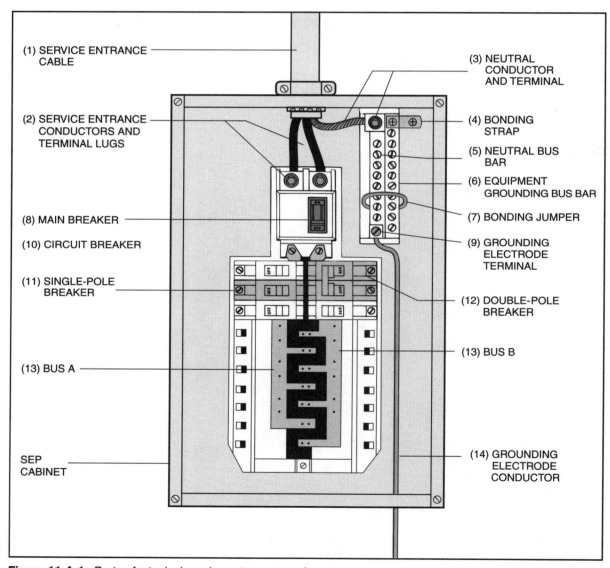

Figure 11-A-1. *Parts of a typical service entrance panel.*

■ Parts of a Service Entrance Panel

(1) **Service Entrance Cable /Conductors -** conductors that provide power from the utility service drop to the service entrance panel.

(2) **Main Lug Terminals -** terminals to which the service entrance cable ungrounded conductors are connected.

(3) **Neutral Conductor and Terminal -** terminal located on power/neutral bar to which service entrance neutral conductor is connected.

(4) **Bonding Strap -** bonds the equipment grounding bus bar to SEP cabinet.

(5) **Neutral Bus Bar -** the termination point for connecting all grounded circuit conductors to the SEP.

(6) **Equipment Grounding Bus Bar -** termination point for connecting all equipment grounding conductors to the SEP.

(7) **Bonding Jumper -** provides a bonding connection between the equipment grounding bus bar, neutral bus bar and the grounding electrode system.

(8) **Grounding Electrode Terminal-**located on the neutral bar. Connects the electrical wiring system to the grounding electrode conductor.

(9) **Main Breaker -** main breaker s provide protection and controls the electrical current entering the service entrance panel. The main breaker contains two internal switches with overcurrent protection. Each switch provides a disconnect for onehalf of the power bus bar.

(10) **Circuit Breakers -** provide overcurrent protection for each of the ranch circuits in the system. They will provide protection from continued overloads or short circuit problems. When tripped, the switch on each breaker may be reset and provide easy "on-off" access when making repairs. They are designed to carry up to 80% of their ampere rating on a continuous basis.

(11) **Single-Pole Circuit Breaker -** type of overcurrent protection device used for the circuit protection and current control for 120-volt branch circuits.

(12) **Double-Pole Circuit Breaker -** type of overcurrent protection device used for protecting and controlling current to 240-volt branch circuits.

(13) **Power Bus -** equipment that conducts electrical current from the service entrance conductors, through the main breaker to each of the circuit breakers. The circuit breakers, in turn, provide protection and pass along current to the branch circuits. The power bus bar is designed as two parts; A and B. Each is controlled by the main breaker. The positions on the bus bar to which the breakers are installed, are commonly called **stabs.**

- Single-pole circuit breakers are installed alternately to the (A) side of the bus bar and then to the (B) side of the same bus bar. Succeeding single-pole breakers are installed in the same sequence.

- Double-pole circuit breakers are installed to both (A) and (B) sides of the bus bar.

(14) **Grounding Electrode Conductor -** connects the electrical wiring system to the to the supplemental grounding electrode.

■ Types of Service Entrance Panels

There are essentially two types of service entrance panels used in most residential wiring systems:

1. A SEP with main breaker (installed inside the residence).

2. A combination meter/SEP with main breaker disconnect (installed outside the residence).

For some time, it has been an accepted practice to locate the service entrance panel inside the residence in some out-of-the-way location. This appeared to be convenient place for both electrical contractors and homeowners. Locations like hallways, closets and storage areas inside attached garages were common locations. Placing the SEP in these areas worked well until problems occurred later. It is not uncommon for a service conductor to fail years after its installation because a nail was driven into the installation during construction—or for a variety of other reasons. Not only do conditions like this make repairs difficult, they can also be extremely hazardous.

Today the NEC® requires that service entrance panels be located in accessible areas either outside or inside the structure near a point where the service conductors enter the residence. This requirement has been part of the NEC® for many years, however local codes are beginning to enforce this regulation. Local codes may require even more specific locations for service entrance panel installations. Always check with you local electrical inspection office and the utility supplier before selecting a location.

Figure 11-A-2 below illustrates a typical SEP installation located on an inside wall of the residence.

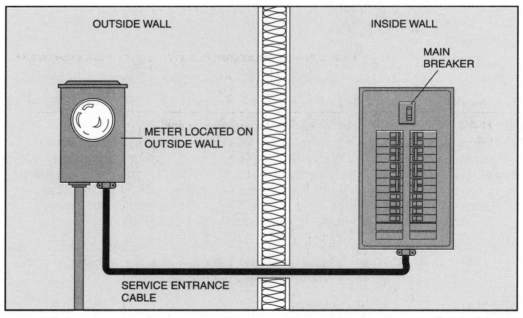

Figure 11-A-2. *A typical service entrance panel with main breaker installed inside the residence.*

Many local electrical codes now require the installation of a **combination meter/service entrance panel with a main breaker disconnect (Figure 11-A-3).** This type of SEP arrangement is located outside the residence for easy service access. It also provides immediate access in emergency situations where disconnecting power to the residence is essential.

In addition to installing the main disconnect in an easy access location outside the residence, branch circuits may also originate from this source. These branch circuits, which will likely include a subpanel feeder circuit, may also supply power to some of the larger circuits in the system which may be located near the service entrance. These might include a water heater, clothes dryer and heating and cooling systems. Smaller branch circuits such as lighting and receptacles are usually supplied by the subpanel located inside the residence. This type of SEP/disconnect arrangement makes it convenient and less expensive to run large equipment branch circuits from this location because the circuit runs are usually shorter and require fewer feet of electrical cable.

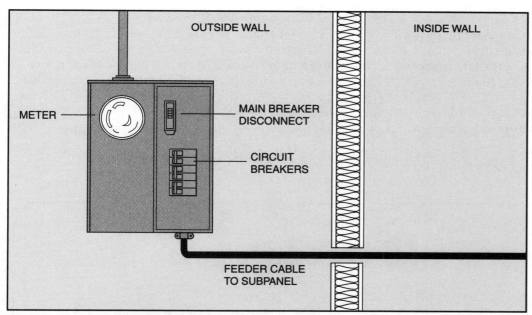

Figure 11-A-3. *A combination meter base and service entrance panel with main breaker disconnect.*

■ Installing the Service Entrance Panel

Before branch circuits can be installed in the SEP, the panel board must be prepared to accept them. This includes the installation of the service entrance conductors, neutral and equipment grounding bus bars and grounding electrode conductor.

Figure 11-A-4 illustrates the basic SEP equipment installations that must be made before branch circuit installation can begin.

① **Connect both hot (ungrounded) service entrance conductors to the main breaker (Line) terminals.**

Most main breaker terminals are hexagonal and will require the use of an Allen wrench or a torque wrench and should be tightened to the manufactures specifications. Other terminal types, depending on the manufacturer, may be slotted and will require only a regular screwdriver.

② **Connect the neutral service entrance conductor to the terminal on the neutrall bus bar.**

③ **Bond the equipment grounding bus bar to the metal panel cabinet.**

Secure the equipment grounding bus bar to the metal SEP cabinet with a bonding strap. The grounding screw must be green.

④ **Bond the neutral bar to the equipment grounding bus bar with a jumper.**

⑤ **Connect the grounding electrode conductor to the terminal.**

Author's Note:
A bonding jumper is required in service entrance panel boards for bonding the neutral and equipment grounding bus bars.

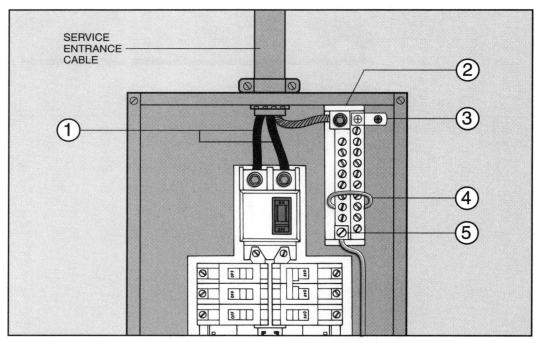

Figure 11-A-4. *It is good wiring practice to first install the basic equipment necessary for the panel board to receive branch circuits*

Good Wiring Practice

Overheating in the SEP can sometimes occur after they are placed into service. Heat build-up may be caused by excessive wire length and/or poor breaker terminal connections. It may even be caused by the placement of the circuit on the panel board. Circuits that require greater power use, such as ranges and clothes dryers should always be located at the top of the panel board near the main breaker. This minimizes overheating and possible voltage drops. Circuits that require less power to operate can be located at the lower end of the cabinet. To help reduce excessive heat build-up, you should make sure that all terminals connections are securely made.

Conductors that are too long not only take up precious space inside the SEP cabinet, they may also cause overheating. Conductors that are too short can likewise cause problems. Conductors should always contain gradual bends. Sharp bends may cause conductors to overheat and fail during an overload on the circuit. Good wiring practice and good judgement suggests allowing enough conductor length for making the necessary terminal connections and for permitting adjustments on the panel board should future circuit additions or changes require it. **Figure 11-A-5** illustrates a subpanel installation in which good wiring techniques have been practiced.

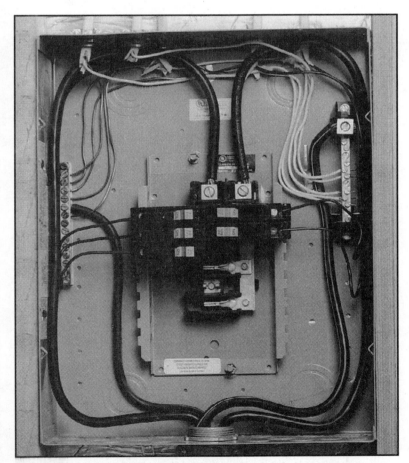

Figure 11-A-5. Good judgement, future use and where the breakers are positioned on the panel board should help you determine the length of the branch circuit conductors.

■ Planning a Service Entrance Panel Layout Schedule

Service entrance panel and subpanel layout schedules, while not required by the NEC®, can be very useful to both the electrical installer and the homeowner. A layout schedule is a guide which can help the electrical installer in planning where the branch circuits should be placed on the panel board. A panel board layout schedule is recommended for the following reasons:

1. It helps the electrician in determining the total number and type of circuit breakers needed.

2. It helps the electrician determine the panel board size by identifying the total number stab positions required. (1) stab position is required for single-pole breakers while (2) stab positions are required for double-pole breakers.

3. It helps in determining the placement of breakers in the panel board to achieve an equal electrical load balance (phase balance).

4. It provides a circuit directory for the homeowner to easily locate and identify circuits and circuit breakers.

Figure 11-A-6 illustrates an example of a SEP layout schedule indicating the breaker rating, circuit name and the position it occupies on the panel board.

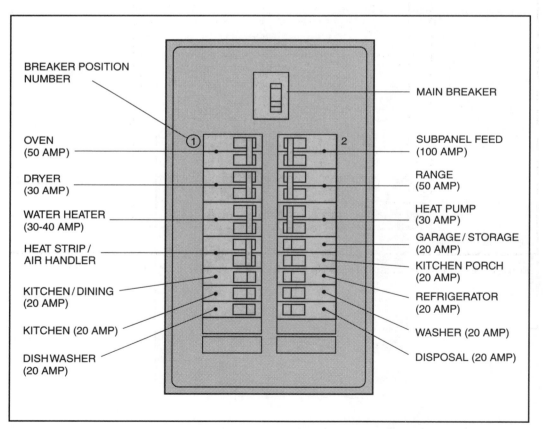

Figure 11-A-6. *A breaker layout schedule showing the placement of breakers on the panel board.*

Figure 11-A-7 illustrates a slightly modified version of the panel board schedule shown in Figure 11-A-6 on page 184. This version should be completed by the electrical installer after all circuits have been installed and tested to make sure they work properly. It should be installed on the inside of the panel box door for easy homeowner reference. It generally indicates the breaker number and the name of the room or area served by that circuit.

Service entrance panel and subpanel schedules should be considered as part of the wiring installation process and should given the attention that is afforded other parts of the wiring installation.

BREAKER SCHEDULE			
1	OVEN	2	SUBPANEL FEED
3	OVEN	4	SUBPANEL FEED
5	DRYER	6	RANGE
7	DRYER	8	RANGE
9	WATER HEATER	10	HEAT PUMP
11	WATER HEATER	12	HEAT PUMP
13	AIR HANDLER / HEAT STRIP	14	GARAGE /STORAGE
15	AIR HANDLER / HEAT STRIP	16	KITCHEN /PORCH
17	KITCHEN / DINING APPLIANCE# 1	18	REFRIGERATOR
19	KITCHEN APPLIANCE# 2	20	CLOTHES WASHER
21	DISHWASHER	22	DISPOSAL
23	(BLANK)	24	(BLANK)
25	(BLANK)	26	(BLANK)

Figure 11-A-7. *A layout schedule showing the number and names of the branch circuits.*

B. Subpanels

In today's larger, modern homes, it has become common practice to install two types of panel boards: a **service entrance panel** and a **subpanel**.

The subpanel, when used in addition to the SEP, is often installed to eliminate the need for long branch circuit runs and to provide additional circuit breaker positions for branch circuits.

While the SEP may be located inside or outside the residence, the subpanel is usually located inside the residence and central to the area it will serve. The subpanel may also be positioned adjacent to the SEP if more breaker positions are needed at that location.

Electrical power to the subpanel is supplied by a feeder cable which is connected to a double-pole breaker in the main service panel. The feeder cable, is usually **type SER (service entrance round)** cable consisting of four conductors; two hot insulated conductors, one insulated neutral and a bare or insulated grounding conductor. When installing an insulated grounding conductor, care must be taken to distinguish it from the other conductors. It may be green in color or reidentified as a grounding conductor if other insulation colors are used.

Subpanel installations do not require a main breaker since the main breaker in the SEP also serves as the primary disconnect for both panels. However, it is permissible to install a breaker disconnect in the subpanel as a matter of personal preference.

A subpanel may have equal ampere rating to that of the of SEP. However, the feeder cable is always sized according to the overcurrent protection device rating that controls it. The device, usually a double-pole breaker, <u>must not</u> be greater than the rating of either the feeder cable or the subpanel.

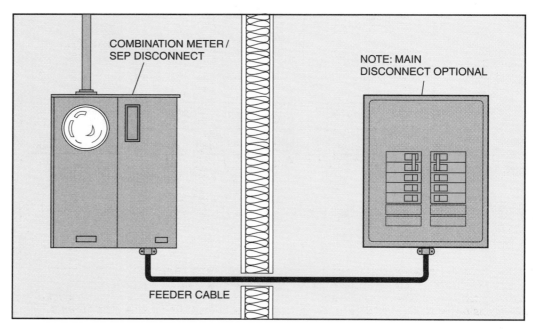

Figure 11-B-1. *Subpanels receive their power from a four-conductor feeder cable (Type SER) installed in the SEP.*

■ Subpanels Requirements

While subpanels perform essentially the same functions as service entrance panels, they differ in their internal design. The primary differences between a service entrance panel and a subpanel are:

1. Subpanels are required to have separate grounding and neutral bus bars. Service entrance panels may have a combined neutral and grounding bus bar.

2. Subpanels receive their power through a four-conductor (SER) feeder cable from the service entrance panel. Both ungrounded conductors terminate at the main lugs on the panel. The grounded conductor terminates at the neutral bus bar and the other terminates at the equipment grounding bus bar.

3. Subpanels are not usually equipped with main breaker disconnects. Ungrounded conductor connections are normally made to on the main lugs. The primary power disconnect for subpanels occur at the service entrance panel main breaker. However, if desired, a main breaker is permitted to be installed in a subpanel. **Figure 11-B-2** illustrates a typical subpanel installation.

Author's Note:
The neutral bus bar in a subpanel is both insulated and isolated from the equipment grounding bus bar.

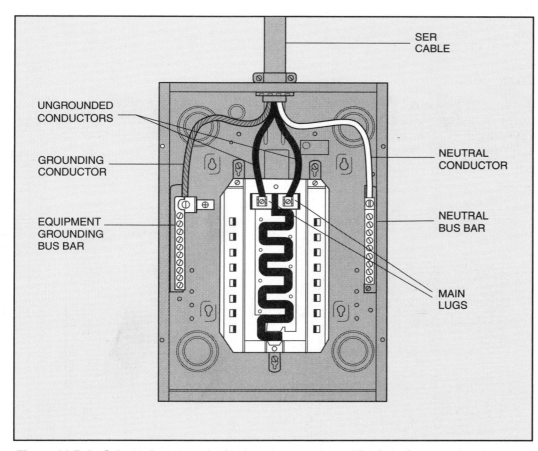

Figure 11-B-2. *Subpanels are required to have separate grounding bars for neutral and grounding conductors. Most subpanels will normally have only main lugs for service conductor connections rather that a main breaker disconnect. However, main breakers are permitted if desired.*

C. Service Entrance Conductors

Cable typically required for service entrance installations are types **SE, USE** and **UF**. They are three-conductor cables usually constructed of copper or aluminum wire and contain two insulated conductors and one, bare neutral conductor. The neutral conductor is made up of smaller wires which are wound around the insulated conductors. The smaller wires must be twisted into a single conductor before installation **(Figure 11-C-1)**. The neutral conductor may sometimes be insulated. When using and insulated neutral conductor, always make sure it is identified as a neutral conductor. It is important that conductors be properly installed and the terminal lugs torqued to the manufacturers specifications.

Type **SER** cable is required as a feeder cable between the subpanel and the SEP. It contains two, insulated hot conductors, an insulated neutral and a grounding conductor, all combined in a round configuration **(Figure 11-C-2)**.

The NEC® requires specific types and sizes of service entrance conductors based on the ampacity requirements of the service entrance panel and subpanel. **Table 11-1** shows the type, ampacity rating and required AWG size of cable conductors typically used in residential wiring.

NEC® References
For more on Service Entrance Cables, see NEC® Articles
230
338
339

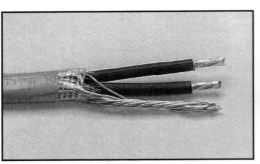

Figure 11-C-1. *Type SE cable contains two insulated conductors and one bare neutral conductor.*

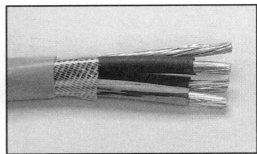

Figure 11-C-2. *Type SER cable contains two insulated conductors, one insulated neutral and one bare grounding conductor.*

Table 11-1
Typical Service Entrance Conductor Sizes

Service entrance ratings	Conductor sizes (AWG)	
	Copper	Aluminum
100	4	2
125	2	1/0
150	1	2/0
200	2/0	4/0
400	400 kcmil	600 kcmil

D. Selecting Service Entrance Panels & Subpanels

Service entrance panels and subpanels are selected based on their ampacity requirements. Ampacity ratings of 100, 150, 200 and 400 amperes are commonly required in today's modern residences.

Panel boards are sized for a particular need based on specific rules required and provided by the NEC®. It requires that residential service equipment be rated at a minimum of 100 amperes when the following conditions exist:

- The calculated load in for the dwelling is 10,000 volt-amperes (10 KVA) or more.

- The dwelling requires 6 or more double-pole breakers (240-volt circuits).

If neither of the above conditions exists, a 60-ampere service panel is allowed. However, very few newly constructed homes today would qualify for such a small amount of electrical service.

From a practical standpoint, you should consider a 100-ampere service panel as a minimum requirement for today's residential electrical demands. However, when considering the installation of items such as electric heating, air conditioning, electric rangers and clothes dryers, water heating and other modern conveniences, 150 or 200-ampere service entrance panels will likely be required.

Figure 11-D-1 below shows some of the different types and sizes of service panels and subpanels available for use in residential electrical systems.

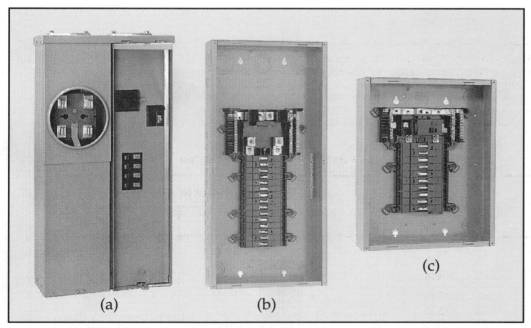

Figure 11-D-1. *Types of service entrance panels. (a) A combination meter/ service panel with main breaker disconnect. (b) a service entrance panel with main breaker. (c) a subpanel service panel.*

■ Calculating SEP & Subpanel Ampacity Ratings

The NEC® provides 2 methods for calculating the minimum SEP and subpanel ampere ratings.

(1) The Standard Method* (multiple demand factors)

(2) The Optional Method (1 demand factor)

Both methods require that **demand factors** be applied when calculating loads. Demand factors are identified as *the ratio of the maximum demand of an electrical system—or part of a system— to the total connected load of a system or part of a system*. Demand factors are applied because all of the connected load will never be energized at the same time. When calculating the demand load, demand percentages for a particular load are based on historical data provided by the NEC®.

Only the Optional method will be discussed here.

▼ The Optional Method

The Optional Method of load calculation will result in an ampacity rating very close to that actually required— and it is much easier to calculate because it requires only one demand factor.   All calculations made in the optional method are rated in **volt-amperes (VA)**. The following demand factors are used in determining the load calculation using the optional method.

- **Small Appliance Circuits**

    Calculate a minimum of two (2) 20-ampere circuits @ 1500 VA (watts) each.

- **Lighting Loads**

    Calculate 3 VA (watts) per square foot of space in the dwelling.

- **Laundry Circuit @1500 VA (watts)**

- **Nameplate ratings of all in-place appliances**

- **All motor loads (KVA ratings. Voltage X Amperes =KVA).**

    Calculate 100% of the first 10 KVA on all loads.

    Calculate 40% of all remaining loads.

- **Select the larger of the following loads:**

    1. **100% of the nameplate rating of air conditioning and cooling equipment including heat pump compressors and strip heaters.**

    2. **100% of nameplate ratings of electric thermal storage and other heating systems.**

    3. **65% of nameplate ratings of central electric and space heating equipment including integral supplemental heating in heat pumps.**

    4. **40% of nameplate rating of electric space heating equipment that includes four or more separately controlled units.**

Figure 11-D-2 (opposite page) shows an example of how to calculate the load demand for determining the size of a service panel of a typical size home.

The load calculations shown in the form below are based on a 2000 square foot residence with an air conditioning unit and a 10 KW electric furnace. A blank version of this form can be found on page 256, appendix B.

NEC Article	Circuit Type	Rating		Total Calculated Load
		Load Calculations (Optional Method)		
220-3b(2)	Lighting	_3_ VA **X** _2,000_ sq. ft.		_6,000_ VA
210-52b	Small Appliance	_1,500_ VA **X** 2 circuits		_3,000_ VA
220-16b	Laundry	_1,500_ VA **X** 1 circuit		_1,500_ VA
	Fixed Appliances	**Nameplate Ratings**		
220-3b(3)	Range	_____ KVA		_____ KVA
220-30	Oven	_5.0_ KVA		_5.0_ KVA
	Cook Top	_6.0_ KVA		_6.0_ KVA
	Garbage Disposal	_____ KVA		_____ KVA
	Dishwasher	_1.2_ KVA		_1.2_ KVA
	Trash Compactor	_____ KVA		_____ KVA
	Clothes Dryer	_5.0_ KVA		_5.0_ KVA
	Water Heater	_4.5_ KVA		_4.5_ KVA
	Other	_____ KVA		_____ KVA
	Total: All Circuits			_____ KVA
220-30	**Demand Factors:**			
	10 KVA @ 100%	_10 KW_		_10,000_ KVA
	Remainder @ 40%	_23 KVA X 40%_		_9,200_ KVA
	Select Larger of the following (use name plate rating)			
	100% of AC or Heat Pump	_4.08_ KVA		_____ KVA
	100% of thermal storage (or other heating systems)	_____ KVA		_____ KVA
	65% of Central Electric Furnace and Heat Pump Strip Heat (if less than 4 units)	_6.5_ KVA		_6.5_ KVA
	65% of Electric Space Heaters	_____ KVA		_____ KVA
	40% of Electric Space Heaters (if more than 4 units)	_____ KVA		_____ KVA
	Total KVA: All Loads			_25,700_ KVA
	Minimum Service Panel			
	$\frac{25,700}{240\,V}$ = 107 Amps	**Recommended Panel Size =** _125 Amperes_		

Figure 11-D-2. A load calculation table (optional method).

■ Determining the Number of Circuit Breakers

By counting the number of circuits that are installed in the wiring plan, and the the single-and double-pole breakers and the stab positions they will occupy on the panel board will help you determine the determine the size of panelboard that will be required. Remember that 240-volt breakers require two positions (stabs) on the bus bar while 120-volt breakers require only one position. **Table 11-2** below shows some of the breaker requirements for typical branch circuits

Always consider planning for future circuit needs when calculating the size of panel board. You will want to install a panel with additional circuit breaker positions to accommodate expected— or unexpected future growth.

In chapter 3, *Planning Circuits,* you learned a simple method for determining the number of general purpose circuits based on a factor of one circuit per 500 square ft. of floor space. Using the load demand calculations shown in Figure 11-D-2 , you can also determine the required number of general purpose circuits using the following factors:

For 20-ampere circuits: $\dfrac{10,000 \ (\text{KVA Load Demand})}{2400 \ (\text{Amps X Volts})} = 5$ Circuits (Minimum)

For 15-ampere circuits: $\dfrac{10,000 \ (\text{KVA Load Demand})}{1800 \ (\text{Amps X Volts})} = 6$ Circuits (Minimum)

Table 11-2
Circuit Breaker Requirements for Typical Branch Circuits

Circuit Types	Single-Pole Breakers	Double-Pole Breakers
General Lighting/Wall Receptacles	5	
Small Appliances	2 (minimum)	
Laundry	1	
Garbage Disposal	1	
Dishwasher	1	
Garbage Compactor	1	
Attic Fan (Whole House)	1	
Range		1
Oven		1
Cooktop Unit		1
Clothes Dryer		1
Water Heater		1
Central Air Conditioning		1
Heat Pump		1
Electric Furnace		1
Subpanel Feeder Breaker		1
Outbuilding Feeder Breaker		1
Space Heaters		1
Outdoor Recptacles	(Variable)	

Grounding the Electrical Wiring System

12

Grounding the electrical wiring system is fundamental to the safety of those installing, using and servicing the electrical system.

It also assures the system will work properly while preventing damage to the system and to the residence in which it is installed. Grounding the residential electrical system covers all non-current carrying parts of the electrical installation, including the wiring in the SEP and all circuits connected to the SEP.

The National Electric Code ® requires that <u>all</u> electrical systems serving a home must be bonded together. These include the electrical wiring system, telephone system, cable television system, burglar alarm system or any other electrical system installed in the home. Bonding each of these systems into a common grounding electrode system reduces differences in potential between them which may be caused by power surges, lightning strikes or other types of ground fault occurrences. Grounding electrodes typically used in grounding residential electrical systems are usually made of metal rods driven into direct contact with the earth **(Figure 12-1)**.

NEC® Reference
For more on grounding, see NEC® Article 250

Figure 12-1. *A grounding electrode conductor metal grounding rod are visible signs that the electrical wiring system has been grounded.*

To understand the concept of "grounding" the electrical system, you must first understand the meaning the terms, *grounding, grounded* and *bonding*. Often these terms are used interchangeably, but technically each has a different and specific meaning.

- **Grounding** is the process of making a planned, continuous, connection (grounding path) between all the **non-current carrying** parts of the electrical wiring installation and the earth or some other conducting body. This includes <u>all</u> materials and devices used in the residential circuits and in the service entrance panels and subpanels.

- **Grounded** is the term that describes the act of being connected to the earth or to some conducting body that serves in place of the earth.

NEC® Reference
For more on
bonding, see
NEC® Article
250 - Section G

- **Bonding** is the process in which all **non-current carrying** metallic parts of the residential wiring system (circuits, service entrance equipment, metal water and gas pipes) in the residence are permanently joined together to form a continuous grounding path. When a ground fault or short circuit is experienced in the system, electrical current is safely conducted in this grounding pathuring. When used in this context, non-current carrying refers to any part of a electrical device, appliance or equipment which does not—and is not intended— to conduct electrical current.

In this chapter you will learn the importance of grounding the total electrical system and the options available to you on how to achieve a properly grounded system. Each phase of the grounding system, what is required and how it is installed will be discussed under the following topics:

A. The Electrical Grounding System

B. Grounding Electrodes

A. The Electrical Grounding System

Grounding the electrical wiring system is accomplished by connecting the grounding terminals of all the devices and equipment that comprise the electrical wiring system into a single system. This includes circuits, receptacles, switches, cables, outlet boxes, appliances, equipment, SEP and subpanel. These must be connected to all other systems installed in the residence such as metal water piping systems, metal gas pipes, telephone, cable television and home security systems. After all systems have been bonded together, it is then grounded to the earth by one of several approved methods.

Figure 12-A-1 illustrates a simple diagram for grounding a clothes washer circuit. The grounding conductor in the power cord is bonded to the washer frame at the terminal block. At the receptacle, the equipment ground in the circuit cable is connected from the receptacle grounding terminal to the equipment grounding bus in the SEP. The grounded circuit conductor is connected to the neutral bus and the ungrounded (black) conductor is connected to the breaker. The circuit is now installed and grounded.

The grounding electrode conductor connects the non-current carrying parts (metallic water pipe and other electrical systems) of the electrial wiring system to the supplemental grounding electrode installed in contact with the earth. This electrode is usually installed on the exterior of the dwelling. Should accidental contact between the ungrounded conductors make contact with the frame or equipment in the washer, a short circuit will result causing the circuit breaker to trip, de-energizing the circuit.

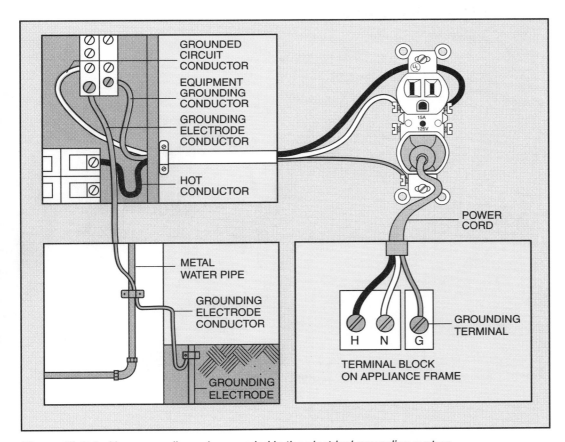

Figure 12-A-1. How an appliance is grounded in the electrical grounding system.

Circuit and Equipment Grounding

As you've already learned, all circuit devices appliances and equipment connected to the circuit until they ultimately reach their termination point in the service entrance panel.

In every circuit, the **grounded** or **neutral** conductor in the circuit terminates at the neutral and/or grounding bus bars in the SEP or subpanel **(Figure 12-A-2)**.

Equipment grounding refers to those parts of the electrical system that do not— and are not intended to carry current. These include metal equipment frames, metal cabinets that enclose appliances, motors, metal device and outlet boxes, switches receptacles and metal conduit.

The NEC® requires that electrical equipment must be bonded to the equipment grounding bus in order to:

- Limit the voltage to ground on equipment frames and on metal enclosure used in the wiring system.

- Assure operation of overcurrent devices in case of ground fault occurrences.

Equipment grounding is accomplished by means of the grounding conductor installed to the grounding terminals on receptacles, switches, metal outlet boxes, or other types of equipment installed on the circuit.

The grounding conductors from each circuit also terminate in the SEP or subpanel at the equipment grounding bus bar.

NEC® Reference
For more on circuit and equipment grounding, see NEC® Article 250-Section E

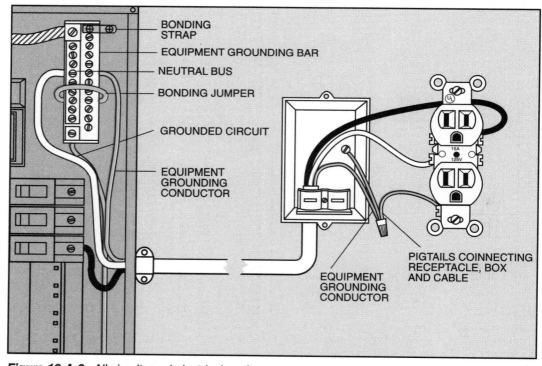

Figure 12-A-2. *All circuits and electrical equipment must be grounded in the SEP.*

Service Entrance Grounding

The equipment grounding bus bar must be **bonded** to the SEP cabinet with a **bonding strap (Figure 12-A-3)**. The bonding strap assures that the equipment grounding bus bar and the SEP are now part of the grounding system and offers additional protection against ground faults that may occur. The NEC® requires that a green screw be used to connect the bonding strap to the SEP cabinet. This green screw indicates a grounding terminal. It is required to be visible after being installed.

If the SEP cabinet is made from a nonmetallic material, no bonding strap is necessary. However, the neutral bar must be bonded to the equipment grounding conductor in the service entrance panel.

The NEC® requires that a service entrance panel contain both a **neutral bus bar** and an **equipment grounding bus** bar. These must be bonded together with a **bonding jumper**. When additional terminals are needed for both the neutral bus and equipment grounding bus, they may be purchased separately and installed in the SEP. An additional bus must also be bonded to the existing bus with a bonding jumper **(Figure 12-A-4)**.

The NEC® also requires that subpanels must have a separate equipment grounding bus bar and neutral bus bar (see Figure 11-B-2, page 187). The grounding bus and the neutral bus must not be bonded together in a subpanel.

NEC® Reference
For more on main bonding jumpers, see NEC® Article 250-79

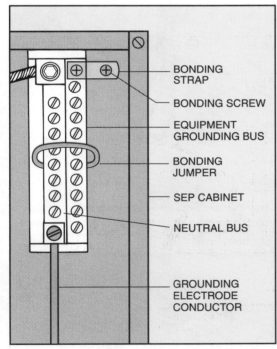

Figure 12-A-3. *The equipment grounding bus must be bonded to the SEP cabinet with a bonding strap. The bonding screw must be green in color.*

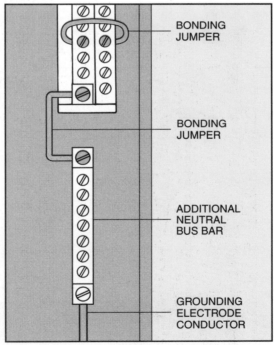

Figure 12-A-4 *Some service entrance panels may contain additional neutral and equipment grounding bars. If this arrangement exists, they must be bonded together with a bonding jumper.*

B. The Grounding Electrode System

All electrical wiring systems must be grounded using an approved bonding and grounding electrode system. **NEC® Article 250-50** describes the variety of options and materials available for use as grounding electrodes. You must be able to determine which of these options is available to you and which is required by your local building code. Two methods for grounding the residential electrical system are shown below. The system may also be grounded at the neutral bus bar in the service entrance panel (see Figure 12-B-5, page 200).

NEC® Reference For more on the grounding electrode system, see NEC® Articles 250-24(c) 250-32 250-50

Figure 12-B-1 illustrates the method commonly used in many areas. A grounding electrode conductor is installed to a grounding terminal in the meter base. It is then connected to a supplemental grounding electrode, a rod usually made of iron, steel or copper, installed to a depth of 8 ft. in the earth.

Figure 12-B-2 illustrates the grounding electrode conductor connected at the service entrance head to the neutral grounding conductor. It is also connected to a supplemental grounding electrode (rod) which has been installed in the earth.

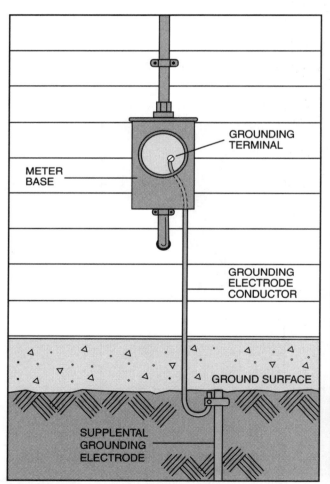

Figure 12-B-1. *The electrical wiring system may be grounded at the meter base .*

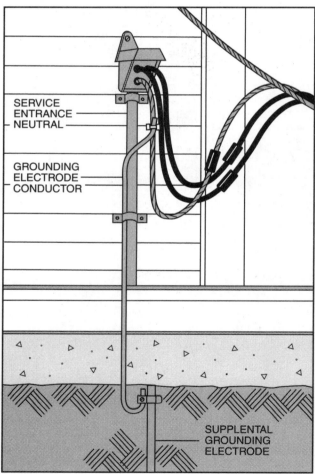

Figure 12-B-2. *The wiring system may also be grounded at the serviced entrance head.*

The interior metal water piping system in a residence must always be bonded to either the service entrance panel cabinet, the grounding electrode conductor or the grounding electrode. Other metal piping which may likely become accidentally energized, such as gas pipes, must also be bonded to the electrical grounding system. The bonding of all these elements will insure a continuous electrical path to safely conduct current that may accidentally be imposed on it.

Figure 12-B-3 below illustrates a typical method of bonding the metal water piping system to the grounding system. Another typical method of bonding metal piping is shown in **Figure 12-B-4.** It illustrates how a **bonding jumper** is used to continue the electrical path around a water meter. This method insures that the grounding path will be continuous should the pipe connections to the water meter become loose, or if the meter should be constructed of a nonmetallic material unsuitable for creating an adequate grounding path.

NEC® Reference
For more on bonding metal water piping systems, see NEC® Articles 250-50(a) 250-104(b)

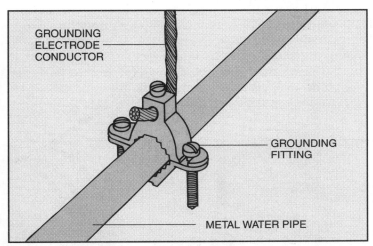

Figure 12-B-3. Metallic water systems are bonded to the electrical grounding system by a grounding electrode conductor and a grounding fitting.

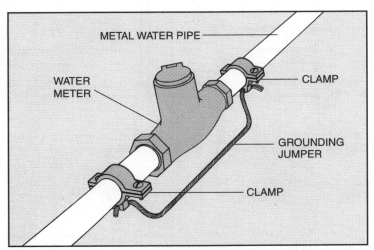

Figure 12-B-4. A bonding jumper must be used to create a continuous grounding path around devices such as water meters installed in the metallic water pipe system.

■ Types of Grounding Electrodes

The NEC® identifies specific types of electrode materials for use in special types of grounding situations and conditions. **NEC® Article 250** covers a variety of options for bonding and grounding the electrical system. You must decide which of these grounding options is available to you and which is permitted by your local building code. It requires that each of the following types of electrodes, if available for use at the structure, <u>must be bonded</u> with the others to form the grounding electrode system.

NEC® Reference
For more on using
metal waterpipe as
a type of grounding
electrode, see
NEC® Article
250-50
250-50a
250-50a (2)

1. **Metal Underground Water Pipes** - When available, metal water pipes must be bonded to the supplemental grounding electrode and to the neutral bus bar in the service entrance panel. This connection must be made to the water pipe within the first 5 ft. after it enters the residence **(Figure 12-B-5)**. The water pipe must also be in direct contact with the earth for at least 10 ft. to be considered an effective grounding electrode.

   Today, many local codes permit the use of nonmetallic water piping in new construction. Clearly, when nonmetallic water piping cannot be used as part of the grounding system, other grounding options must be used. However, when metallic water piping is used in a residence, it must be used as part of the grounding electrode system— together with any available combination of the following methods for grounding the electrical system.

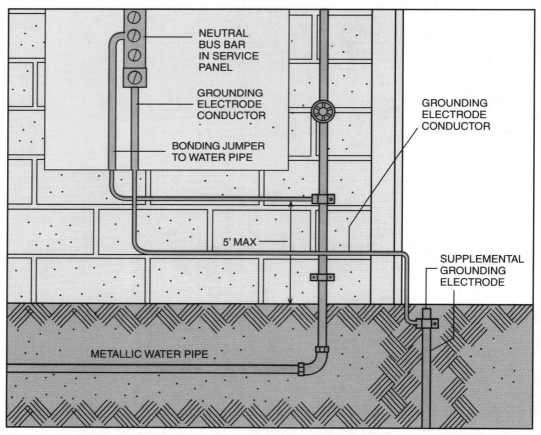

Figure 12-B-5. When available, all metallic water pipes must be bonded to the grounding system.

2. **Concrete Encased Electrodes -** An electrode encased in a foundation footing covered by at least 2 inches of concrete must be used if available. The electrode must be at least 20 ft. in length and consist of one or more 1/2 -inch steel reinforcing bars **(Figure 12-B-6)**.

3. **Ground Ring -** A grounding ring of bare copper wire at least No. 2 AWG or larger that encircles the residence for a length of at least 20 ft. **(Figure 12-B-7)**. The electrode, when used for this type of installation, must be buried to a depth of at least 2-1/2 ft.

4. **Metal Framework -** The metal frame of a building may also be used to form the grounding electrode system. However, it is not applicable to most residential construction and will not be discussed here.

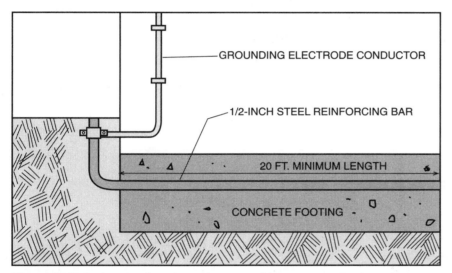

Figure 12-B-6. *A grounding electrode encased in a concrete footing.*

NEC® Reference
For more on concreteencased electrodes, ground rings and metal building frames, see NEC® Articles 250-50 (b) 250-50 (c) 250-50 (d)

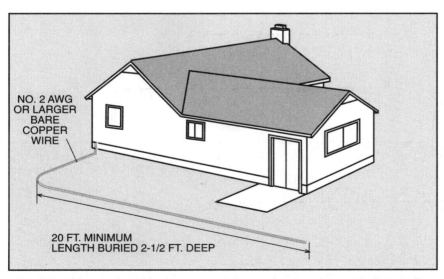

Figure 12-B-7. *A grounding ring of bare copper wire may be used where soil conditions do not permit grounding rods.*

■ Supplemental (Made) Electrodes

Supplemental, or **made** electrodes, are typically made from metal rods, metal pipes or metal plates. Where practical, they must be buried below the permanent moisture level of the earth and must be free of paint or enamel coatings.

Typical supplemental electrodes are:

NEC® Reference
For more on
supplemental
(made) electrodes,
see NEC® Articles
250-52 (c)
250-54
250-56
250-118

1. **Rod and Pipe Electrodes -** Iron or steel rod electrodes must be at least 5/8-inch in diameter. Pipe must be at least 3/4-inch trade size or larger and must be galvanized or metal coated for corrosion protection. Pipe or rod electrodes must not be less than 8 ft. in length and installed to a depth of at least 8 ft. in direct contact with the earth **(Figure 12-B-8)**.

    Non-ferrous rods must be listed and not less than 1/2-inch in diameter. Stainless steel rods must also be at least 1/2-inch in diameter. The top of the electrode must be flush with or below ground level unless it and the grounding conductor or both protected from physical damage **(Figure 12-B-9)**.

    Where electrodes cannot be driven more than 4 ft. deep into the earth because of ground rock or other obstructions, they may be driven at an oblique angle not to exceed 45° from vertical **(Figure 12-B-10)**. At least 8 ft. of the electrode must be in physical contact with the earth.

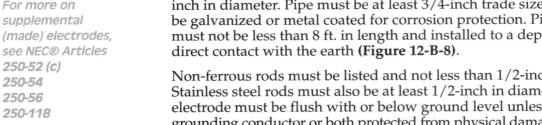

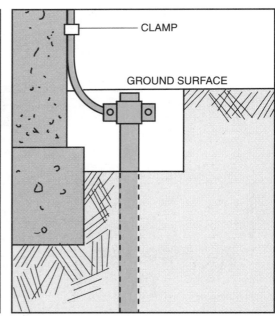

Figure 12-B-8. *Supplemental ground rods must be at least 5/8-inch in diameter.*

Figure 12-B-9. *The top of supplemental ground rods must be driven below the ground surface for protection.*

When more than one electrode grounding rod is used, each electrode must be installed <u>not less</u> than 6 ft. Apart and must be bonded together with an approved bonding jumper to form a single grounding electrode system **(Figure 12B-11)**.

2. **Plate Electrodes** - Plate electrodes may also be used where it is not possible to use a grounding rod or grounding ring. The plate electrode must be at least 1/4 - inch thick if made of iron or steel. Non-ferrous metal plates must be at least 0.06 inches thick. The plate must be at least 2 ft. square and placed in contact with the earth at a depth of not less than 2-1/2 ft. **(Figure 12-B-11)**

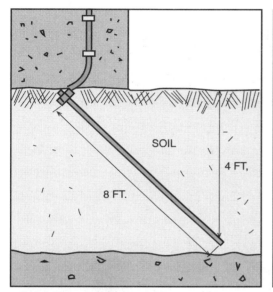

Figure 12-B-10. *Grounding rods are permitted driven into the earth at a 45° under certain soil conditions.*

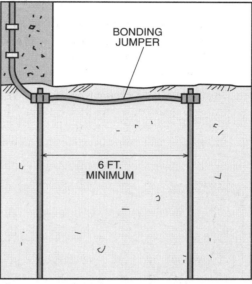

Figure 12-B-11. *Where two grounding rods are used, they must be at least six feet apart and bonded together with a bonding jumper.*

NEC® References For more on supplemental electrodes, see NEC® Articles 250-52 250-52 (c)3 250-52d

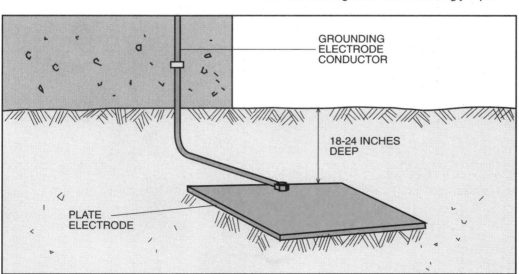

Figure 12-B-11. *Although their use is limited, plate electrodes may be used where conditions do not permit the use of a grounding rods or grounding rings.*

■ Selecting Grounding Electrode Conductors

Selecting the proper size **grounding electrode conductor**, also called the **GEC,** depends upon the equivalent size of the service entrance conductor for the wiring system.

NEC® Reference
For more on
grounding
electrode
conductors, see
NEC® Article
250-64
250-66

For example: if the service entrance conductors are No. 2 AWG copper or smaller, you may use a No. 8 AWG copper grounding electrode conductor. No. 8 AWG copper is required to be enclosed in conduit or armored cable. A No. 6 AWG aluminum grounding electrode conductor is also permitted for use with a No. 2 AWG copper service entrance conductor and may be installed to the surface of the building if not exposed to severe physical damage. **Table 12-1** below shows some common sizes of service entrance conductors and the corresponding grounding electrode conductor size typically used in residential installations. For a complete list of grounding electrode conductors, consult **NEC® Tables 250-66.**

The NEC® permits the use of copper, aluminum or copper-clad aluminum for use as grounding electrode conductors. Aluminum and copper-clad aluminum may not be used in contact with masonry, corrosive conditions or in direct contact with the earth.

Table 12-1			
Grounding Electrode Conductor Size Requirements			
Service Entrance Conductors (AWG)		Grounding Electrode Conductors (AWG)	
Copper	Aluminum or Copper Clad Aluminum	Copper	Aluminum or Copper Clad Aluminum
No. 2 or Smaller	No. 1 or Smaller	8	6
No. 1 or 1/0	2/0 or 3/0	6	4
2/0 or 3/0	4/0 or 250 kcmil	4	2

Installing Circuit Breakers

At this point in the electrical wiring installation process, circuit cables have already been pulled into the SEP and /or subpanel and it is time to install the circuit breakers for each of the branch circuits **(Figure 13-1)**.

A neat, professional wiring installation in the SEP not only looks better, it also allows for better air circulation inside the panel cabinet which reduces heat buildup. It will also make it much easier to identify circuits when troubleshooting a circuit problem or when adding additional circuits to the panel.

In this chapter you will learn how to safely install and remove circuit breakers in the SEP and subpanel. These methods are discussed under the following headings:

A. Safety First!

B. Installing 120 -Volt (Single-Pole) Circuit Breakers.

C. Installing 240 -Volt (Double-Pole) Circuit Breakers.

D. Installing 120 -240-Volt Circuit Breakers.

E. Removing Circuit Breakers.

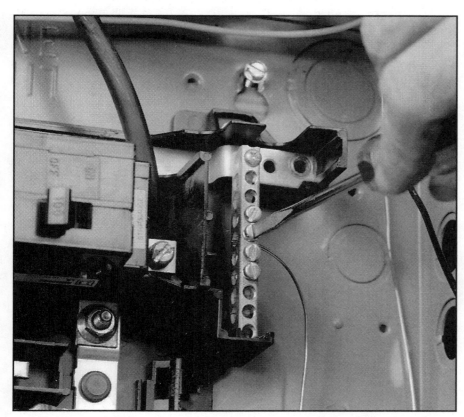

Figure 13-1. *Installing a grounding conductor to the equipment grounding bus bar.*

A. Safety First!

Installing circuit breakers can be done simply and with relative safety —if certain safety procedures are followed. Below are two safety rules that should always be followed before attempting to work on a panel board.

Author's Note
When removing circuit breakers from the panel, always make sure the main breaker is in the OFF position.

Rule #1: Always turn the power off at the main breaker (**Figure 13-A-1**). This should de-energize the panel board on the **load side**. The **load side** is considered those parts of the panel whose power is controlled by the main breaker. This includes the branch circuit breakers, conductors, bus bars, etc. However, simply turning power off at the main breaker <u>does not</u> de-energize the service entrance conductors on the line side of the panel. The **line side** of the panel board is always energized as long as power is supplied to the service entrance. You should always treat the service entrance conductors (**line side**) as energized — and dangerous (**Figure 13-A-2**)!

When working around the panel board, make sure you only work on those areas controlled by the main breaker.

Rule #2: After turning off the power at the main breaker, test the panel board with a volt-meter as an extra safety measure.

You should always remember to practice safe working habits when working on the service entrance panel. Failure to take the time to follow these simple suggestions could mean the difference in life or death.

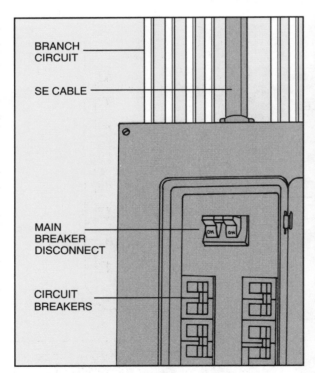

Figure 13-A-1. *Never work on a hot (energized) panel board! Always turn off the power at the main breaker.*

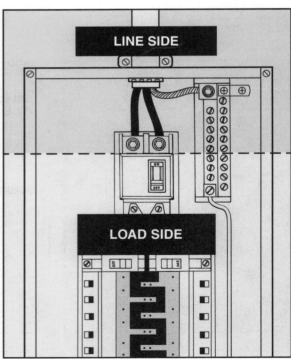

Figure 13-A-2. *The line side of a service panel is always energized. Power to the load side is controlled by the main breaker.*

B. Installing Circuit Breakers

Circuit breakers are installed on a service entrance panel by connecting them to the **bus bar** assembly The bus bar assembly conducts electricity from the hot conductors in the service entrance cable to the circuit breakers. The breakers are attached by contacts in the circuit breakers— **one** for single-pole circuit breakers **(Figure 13-B-1a)** and **two** for double-pole circuit breakers **(Figure 13-B-1b)**. These contacts are snapped into **stab positions** on the bus bars and secured by clips that snap into the slots on the panel board.

Figure 13-B-2 illustrates the principle of how single and double-pole breakers are installed to the stabs on a **straight bus** panel board. The bus bar assembly contains two bars —A and B — both controlled by the main breaker. Each service entrance conductor supplies 120 volts to each **bus bar** or **"leg"** on the assembly. Single-pole circuit breakers are connected to a single bus bar stab in an alternating sequence: A-B-A-B-A-B, etc. Double-pole circuit breakers must be connected to the stabs on both A and B bus bars.

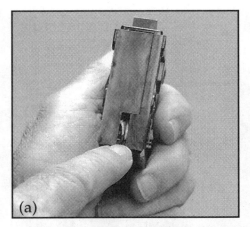

Figure 13-B-1. *(a) Single -pole breakers have only one stab contact. (b) Double-pole breakers have two stab contacts.*

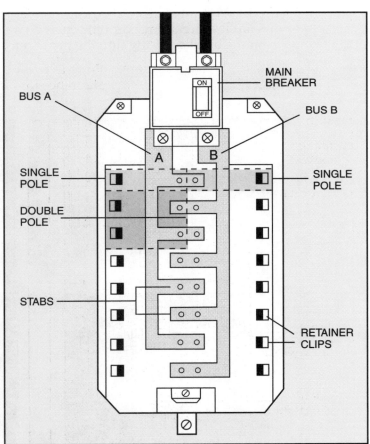

Figure 13-B-2. *Single-pole breakers require only one stab position on either the A or B bus. Double-pole breakers require stab positions on both A and B bus bars.*

C. Installing 120-Volt Circuit Breakers

To install a 120-volt circuit in the SEP/subpanel using a single-pole circuit breaker:

- Strip away the protective cable sheath from the conductors. Make sure there enough conductor length available in the cabinet to make the necessary connections.

- Remove approximately 1/2 -inch insulation from each of the insulated conductors.

- Insert the tip of the **white** conductor into one of the slots in the neutral bus bar and tighten the terminal screw firmly **(Figure 13-C-1a)**.

- Insert the **bare grounding** conductor into the equipment grounding bar and tighten the terminal screw **(Figure 13-C-1b)**.

- Insert the tip of the **black (hot)** conductor under the terminal screw on the circuit breaker and tighten **(Figure 13-C-1c)**.

- Snap the circuit breaker onto the stab on the panel board and press the blade on the breaker firmly into the panel retainer clip **(Figure 13-C-1d)**.

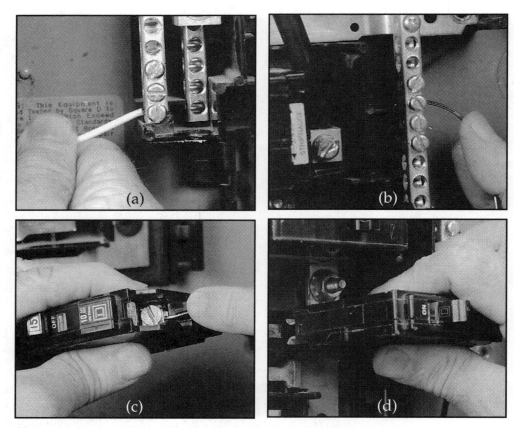

Figure 13-C-1. *Installing a 120-volt (single-pole) circuit breaker.*

D. Installing 240-Volt Circuit Breakers

Electrical equipment such as water heaters, air conditioners and electric space heaters are typically installed on individual 240-volt circuits. Circuit installation for these items will include a double-pole breaker and a 2-conductor cable with equipment ground. Make sure the breaker is rated for the correct amperage required for the appliance/equipment being installed on the circuit.

To install a 240-volt circuit using a double-pole breaker:

- Remove the insulation from each conductor **(Figure 13-D-1a)**.

- Connect the **bare grounding** conductor to the equipment grounding bus bar **(Figure 13-D-1b)**.

- Connect the **black (hot)** conductor to one of the two terminals on the double pole breaker **(Figure 13-D-1c)**.

- Connect the **white conductor** to the remaining terminal on breaker. Remember, <u>the white conductor is not a neutral conductor</u> and must be permanently identified as a **hot conductor (Figure 13-D-1d)**.

- Snap the breaker onto the stabs on both the bus bars until it seats firmly. Press the breaker until it also snaps into the retainer clip on the panel board.

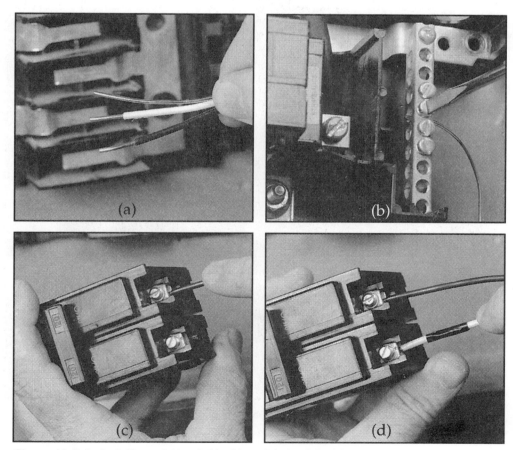

Figure 13-D-1. *Installing a 240-volt (double-pole) circuit breaker.*

E. Installing 120/240-Volt Circuit Breakers

Appliances such as ranges and clothes dry installed on individual circuits usually require both 120 and 240 -volt service. This type of installation requires a double-pole breaker rated for the correct appliance amperage and a 3-conductor with ground cable. This is the current method of installation required by the NEC®. To connect a 120/240-volt circuit using a double-pole breaker:

- Remove the insulation from each of the three insulated conductors **(Figure 13-E-1a)**.

- Connect the **bare grounding** conductor to the equipment grounding bus bar.

- Connect the **white** conductor to the neutral bus bar **(Figure 13-E-1b)**.

- Insert the **red (hot)** conductor under one of the terminal screws on the breaker and tighten firmly **(Figure 13-E-1c)**.

- Insert the black (hot) **conductor** under the remaining terminal screw and tighten firmly **(Figure 13-E-1d)**.

- Snap the breaker onto both stabs on both bus bars and firmly press the breaker until it is seated securely in place under the panel board retainer clip.

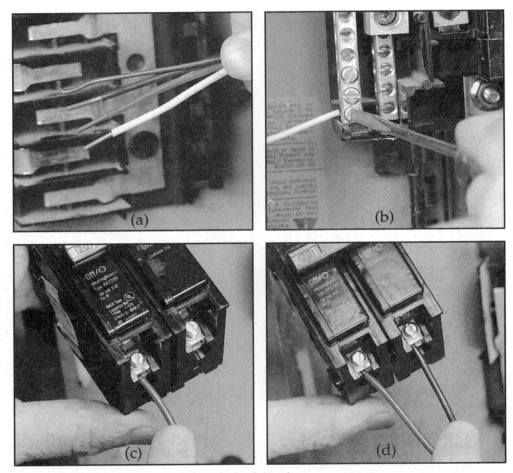

Figure 13-E-1. *Installing a 120/240-volt circuit breaker.*

F. Removing Circuit Breakers

During the breaker installation process, you will likely need to remove, rearrange and replace the circuit breakers to insure they are correctly installed and working properly. It is important that this step be done safely and without damage to the breaker or conductor connections.

Make sure the panel board is not energized! Always make sure the main breaker is in its "OFF"position and then double check with a volt-meter before you begin work.

Removing a circuit breaker from a panel board can be done quite easily with a little "know-how" and the proper technique.

To remove a circuit breaker safely and correctly, follow these simple steps:

- Turn off the power at the main breaker! **(Figure 13-E-1a)**.

- Grasp the breaker firmly and pull outward until it snaps away from its stab on the bus bar **(Figure 13-E-1b)**.

- Gently pull the end of the breaker up and rotate outward until it is released from the panel board retainer clip **(Figure 13-E-1c)**.

- Continue to pull the breaker away from the panel board until it is completely removed **(Figure 13-E-1d)**.

Figure 13-F-1. *Steps for safely removing a circuit breaker.*

Notes

Ground Fault Circuit Interrupters

14

It is important for you to know that **GFCIs are not** designed to protect electrical circuits. They are designed to protect people. Circuit breakers and equipment grounding devices are designed to protect the electrical system. GFCIs are required by the NEC® for use in locations at home or in the workplace where possible danger from electrical shock exists. Since their introduction and adoption, they have proven their value in preventing serious injury —and even death —when properly installed in a circuit.

A GFCI is a much more sensitive device in detecting **current leakage** than the common circuit breaker. Current leakage is commonly known as a **ground fault** or **short circuit.** The GFCI detects this short circuit and breaks the circuit contacts causing electrical current to stop. A convenient feature of GFCIs, particularly receptacle types, is they can be easily tested and reset at the receptacle location rather than at the panel board **(Figure 14-1).**

GFCIs are designed to detect as little as 5 milliamperes of current leakage. While this small amount can be detected by human touch, it is not considered fatal. This amount of current will cause both GFCI receptacles and circuit breakers to trip. By contrast, a current leak of 50 milliamperes will not cause a standard 15ampere circuit breaker to trip. However, this same 50 milliampere current leak can deliver a fatal shock to humans.

In this chapter, you will learn :

A. How GFCIs Work

B. Types of GFCIs

C. Areas Requiring GFCIs

D. Installing GFCIs

Figure 14-1. *A duplex GFCI receptacle equipped with test and reset buttons.*

A. How GFCIs Work

Ground Fault Circuit Interrupters protect people by continually monitoring the current traveling through the hot conductor in the circuit and comparing the current level with the amount of current returning through the neutral conductor in the circuit.

GFCI duplex receptacles, like regular duplex receptacles, are equipped with two sets of contact terminals. Two of the terminals located on one side of the receptacle are marked **Line.** Terminals on the opposite side of the receptacle are marked **Load.** The hot conductors are connected to the darker colored terminals. The white conductors are connecteed to the light or silver colored terminals. They may also be equipped with a green grounding terminal screw.

When a load imbalance of 5 milliamperes occurs in the circuit creating a load imbalance, it is detected by the GFCI. The GFCI trips, breaking the current flow in the circuit **(Figure 14-A-1)**. Once the source of the load imbalance has been identified and corrected, the GFCI can be reset and tested allowing the current flow in the circuit to continue **(Figure 14-A-2)**.

*Author's Note:
Always connect the power source conductors to the line terminals designated on the on the receptacle.*

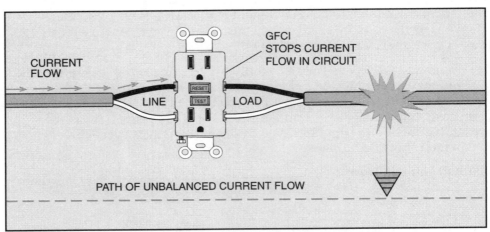

Figure 14-A-1. *A GFCI receptacle breaks the current flow in a circuit when it detects a 5 milliampere imbalance on the circuit.*

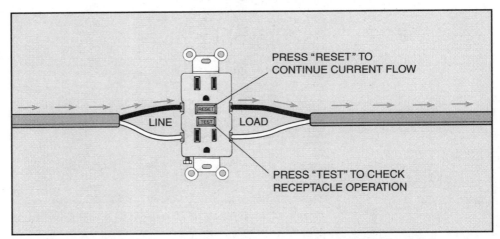

Figure 14-A-2. *After the load imbalance has been corrected, current flow continues by pressing the reset button on the receptacle.*

B. Types of GFCIs

GFCIs are available in three types: **Receptacle, Breaker** and **Portable**

1. **Receptacle GFCI -** These are the most popular style GFCI used in residential electrical circuits **(Figure 14-B-1)**. They are installed at the point of use in the residence and function as a typical duplex receptacles in appearance. The notable exception is that GFCI receptacles are equipped with reset and test buttons which allow the receptacle to be reset and tested after it has tripped. They are available in a variety of colors and sizes and are reasonably priced. Receptacle type GFCIs may be installed to (1) protect an individual outlet or (2) to protect all outlets on the circuit.

   This second option is accomplished by installing a GFCI receptacle in the first outlet on the circuit nearest the point of origin (service entrance panel or subpanel). Should any of the receptacles **downstream** (receptacles installed beyond the first outlet) on this circuit experience a current leakage, the GFCI will trip.

   Consideration should be given not to install too many receptacles on excessively long circuit runs when using this type of installation. Because of the increased conductor length, nuisance tripping of the GFCI may occur.

2. **Breaker Type GFCI -** Breaker style GFCIs can be used in the service entrance or subpanel and will replace a standard breaker **(Figure 14-B-2)**. They are usually rated as 15 and 20-ampere breaker and contain both overcurrent protection and GFCI protection to each receptacle on the circuit.

3. **Portable GFCI -** Portable GFCIs are intended for temporary use such as construction sites or other ares where electrical service is needed on a temporary basis **(Figure 14-B-3)**. They are usually designed to plug into an existing outlet which is protected with a conventional 15 or 20-ampere circuit breaker. While this type of GFCI is necessary for providing safe working conditions on a temporary basis, it should not be used in lieu of the more permanent types of GFCI installations.

Figure 14-B-1. *A GFCI duplex receptacle.*

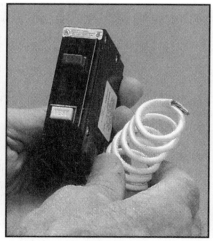

Figure 14-B-2. *A GFCI circuit breaker.*

Figure 14-B-3. *A portable GFCI.*

C. Areas Requiring GFCIs

Ground Fault Circuit Interrupters are required by the National Electrical Code® in all areas of a residence that has been determined to contain possible electrical safety hazards. Listed below are the areas in all new construction that require GFCIs.

- **Bathrooms** - **All** receptacles in a bathroom must have GFCI protection. A bathroom is defined as an area including a basin and one or more toilet, tub or shower.

- **Kitchen Counter Top Receptacles** - **All** 20-ampere kitchen counter top receptacles must have GFCI protection.

- **Garages** - **All** 120-volt,15 and 20-ampere receptacles in garages must have GFCI protection with two exceptions:

  Exception #1: A GFCI **is not** required for an overhead door receptacle because it considered not to be readily accessible.

  Exception #2 : A GFCI **is not** required for outlets that are considered readily accessible because of their location behind a freezer or other similar equipment providing **all** receptacle outlets are occupied by a plug attachment.

- **Outdoor Areas** - **All** outdoor receptacles installed within 6 feet-6-inches of the final grade are considered to be accessible and require GFCI protection.

- **Crawl Spaces and Unfinished Basements** - **All** receptacles in crawl spaces and unfinished basements (below grade), with three exceptions, must have GFCI protection.

  Exception #1: A single receptacle dedicated and identified for use with a refrigerator, freezer or other fixed appliance. A duplex receptacle in which both outlets on the receptacle are occupied with a plug attachment.

  Exception #2: A laundry circuit.

  Exception #3: A single receptacle dedicated to a sump pump.

- **Boathouse Areas** - **All** 120-volt, 15 and 20 -ampere receptacles installed in a boathouse require GFCI protection.

- **Permanently installed pools, storable swimming pools, wading pools, fountains and construction sites** - **All** receptacles serving each of these areas must have GFCI protection.

NEC® Reference
For more on areas
that require GFCI
protection, see
NEC® Articles
210-8
215-9

D. Installing GFCIs

Connecting a portable GFCI is accomplished simply by plugging it directly into a receptacle just as you would any other plug-in device. However, installing receptacle and breaker style GFCIs in a circuit is much like installing standard duplex receptacles and circuit breakers. **Figures 14-D-1, 14-D-2** and **14-D-3** illustrate how duplex receptacle and breaker type GFCIs are installed.

■ Installing Receptacle Style GFCIs

Installing a GFCI protected duplex receptacle can usually be done simply by following the manufacturer's directions that accompany the product. They are installed in standard device boxes in a similar manner as duplex receptacles. **Figure 14-D-1** below illustrates a GFCI receptacle installed to protect all receptacles that follow downstream on the circuit. When installed in this sequence, each receptacle on the circuit following the GFCI receptacle must be labeled *GFCI PROTECTED*.

If the installation is made in a metallic outlet box, the GFCI receptacle must be grounded to the box.

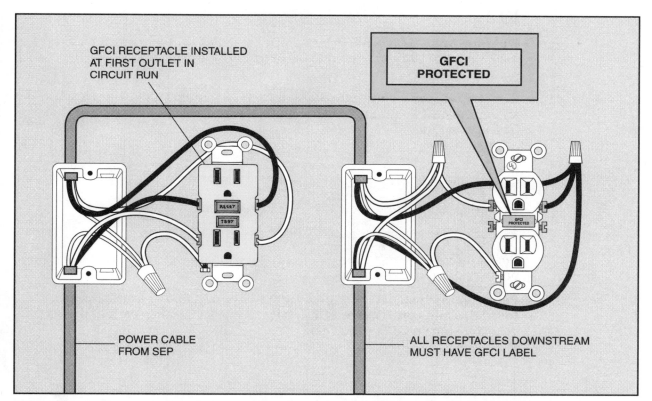

Figure 14-D-1. *Receptacles installed downstream from a GFCI protected circuit must be identified by a stick-on label.*

■ Installing Breaker Style GFCIs

When connecting a breaker style GFCI in a service entrance panel or subpanel, follow the steps as you would for installing a typical 15 or 20 -ampere breaker **(Figure 14-D-2)**:

- Connect the **black** conductor to the terminal on the breaker marked **load**.

- Connect the **white** conductor to the terminal marked **load neutral**.

- Snap the breaker into position on the bus bar and connect the breaker's pigtail conductor to the neutral bus bar on the panel board **(Figure 14-D-3)**.

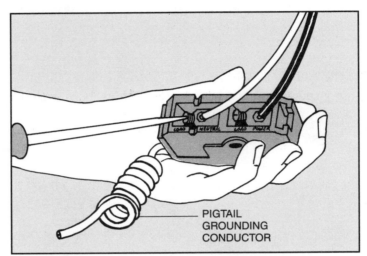

Figure 14-D-2. *Connect the hot and neutral conductors to their designated breaker terminals.*

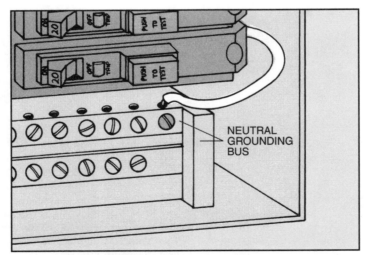

Figure 14-D-3. *Connect the pigtail grounding conductor to the neutral/grounding bar.*

Electrical Conduit

15

Electrical conduit has limited use for the installation of branch circuits in most residential wiring systems **(Figure 15-1)**. However, the NEC® permits— but does not require its use—for service mast installations where minimal clearances are required and for offering physical protection for circuit conductors. While not required by the NEC®, local codes may require its use for both residential and commercial electrical installations. Be sure to check with your local electrical inspection office. Conduit may be **rigid** or **flexible** and made of metal or EPVC. In some cases where flexibility is needed, a **flexible metallic** or **flexible nonmetallic** conduit may be used. This application is often employed when installing an air conditioning unit to the equipment disconnect.

When installing a circuit in electrical metal conduit, individual conductors may be used. An advantage to using metallic conduit is that the conduit may also serve as the equipment grounding conductor. Circuits operating at 120-volts require installed in metallic electrical conduit require only the hot and neutral conductors.

NEC® References for more on electrical conduit, see NEC® Articles
331
345
346
347
348
351-A, B

Where 240-volt circuits are installed in electrical metallic conduit, two (2) hot conductors are required. The electrical conduit may serve as the equipment ground. However, this does not preclude NM sheathed cable from also being used. If a grounding conductor is installed, it may be bear of insulated with a green insulation.

Installing electrical conduit requires some knowledge and assembly skills which are not required when installing nonmetallic sheathed cable.

In this chapter, you will learn some of the basics about electrical conduit— the types available and how to bend and install it.

A. Types of Electrical Conduit

B. Cutting and Bending EMT

C. Installing EMT

D. Installing Conductors in EMT

Figure 15-1. *A duplex receptacle installed using conduit and a metal device box*

A. Types of Electrical Conduit

Rigid Metal Conduit - Made of rigid steel and treated with a rust resistant finish inside and out, it is most often used in residential service installations such as service masts for weatherheads and meter bases. May be threaded and requires threaded fittings for connection. Metal conduit must carry the UL label. Metal water pipe **may not** be substituted for electrical conduit. Available 1/2inch to 6-inch diameters.

Intermediate Metallic Conduit (IMC) - permitted by the NEC® for use where rigid conduit is required in residential wiring installations. Wall thickness is thinner than rigid conduit but thicker than EMT. Available in 1/2-inch to 4-inch diameters.

Electrical Metallic Tubing Conduit (EMT) - also called **"thinwall"**. Lighter and less rigid than both rigid or intermediate metal conduit. Cannot be threaded. Connections made by using special setscrew connectors and/or compression couplings. Available in sizes from 1/2-inch to 4 inches in diameter.

EPVC (Electrical polyvinyl chloride) - a nonmetallic conduit specially developed for electrical applications. Often used in service installations where the support of service equipment (weatherhead, meter, etc.) is not a factor. Economical and may be used in exposed areas in building no more than three stories in height and where not exposed to physical damage.

Flexible metallic conduit - limited to dry locations only and must be protected from physical damage if not covered. May be used for equipment grounding conductor not to exceed 6 ft. Often used when making large appliance and equipment connections.

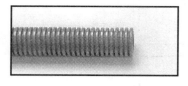

Flexible nonmetallic conduit - sunlight rated for outdoor use. Often used where flexibility is required. Made of circular cross sections, nonmetallic material. Very pliable and easily bent for circuit applications. May not be used where physical damage may occur. Available in sizes 1/2-inch through 2-inch diameters.

Liquidtight flexible conduit - designed for use in wet locations. Made of nonmetallic, sunlight resistant material. May be used for direct burial for building exteriors where flexibility and protection from liquids, vapors and solids is necessary. Connections are made using special liquidtight non-metallic connectors. Available in sizes 1/2-inch to 4 inches.

B. Cutting and Bending EMT

Bending conduit is easily done by using a conduit bender **(Figure 15-B-1)**. Thinwall conduit benders are available for purchase or rental. The benders are marked in 22°, 30°, 45°, and 60° increments indicating the degree of the bend desired **(Figure 15-B-2)**. The foot step on the bender helps to apply steady pressure during the bending process.

Begin the bending process by making careful measurements for the lengths of conduit you will need.

- Cut the conduit to a workable length with a fine blade hacksaw (32 teeth to the inch) or tubing cutter **(Figure 15-B-3)**.

- File or ream the ends of each piece of conduit to remove the sharp, rough edges **(Figure 15-B-4)**. This must be done to prevent damage to the insulation on the conductors as they are pulled through the tubing.

Special care should be taken when bending EMT to avoid kinking or crushing. Measurements are critical when bending conduit. In most in cases it is better to make the necessary bends and then cut the conduit to the finished length.

When bending conduit any run of conduit between outlets, between fittings or between fittings and outlets **must not** contain more than the total equivalent of 4 quarter bends—or 360°.

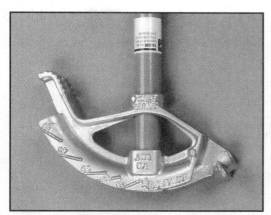

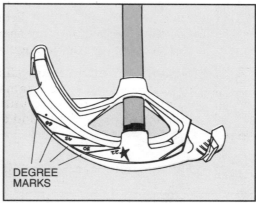

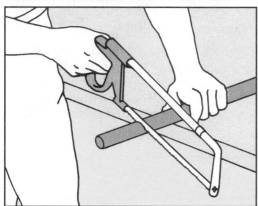

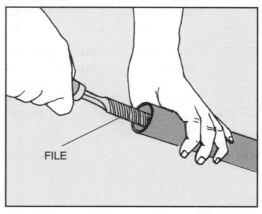

(Top) **Figure 15-B-1.** *A conduit bender.*
(Bottom) **Figure 15-B-3.** *EMT conduit can be easily cut with a hacksaw.*

(Top) **Figure 15-B-2.** *Conduit benders are marked in degrees.*
(Bottom) **Figure 15-B-4.** *Rough edges must be removed to protect conductor insulation.*

■ Creating 45 and 90 Degree Bends

To make a 45°or 90° bend, 11 inches high, using 1/2-inch diameter EMT, follow the sequence of steps illustrated below.

● Place the bender at the correct distance from end of the conduit to arrive at the proper bend. This distance is equal to the desired height of the bend minus the amount of the **"take-up"** height **(Figure 15-B-5a)**. The take-up height is a part of your desired height and is a characteristic of the bender. The take-up height may differ among benders depending on their manufacturer. The typical take-up height for 1/2 -inch EMT is **5 inche**s. To determine where to begin the bend, you must subtract the take-up height of 5 inches (based on 1/2 -inch conduit) from the desired height of 11 inches. This results in a measurement of 6 inches. Measure 6 inches from the end of the conduit and mark the spot. Place the "B" indicator on the bender at this mark **(Figure 15-B-5b)**.

● Keeping the conduit tight against the hard surface of the floor, steadily pull the handle on the bender applying foot and arm pressure. To create a 45° bend, pull the bender handle until it reaches a vertical position to the floor **(Figure 15-B-5c)**.

● To create a 90° bend, continue pulling the bender handle until it reaches a 45° angle to the floor **(Figure 15-B-5d)**. This type of bend is called a **stub-up"**

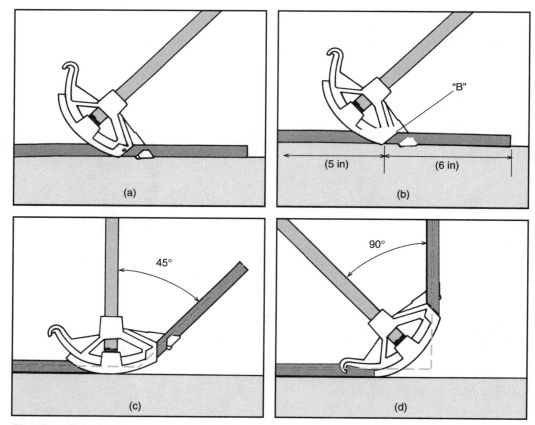

Figure 15-B-5. *Making 45° and 90° bends.*

■ Making Offset Bends

Offset bends are a common part of installing metal conduit **(Figure 15-B-6a)**. They allow the conduit to follow a straight path into the outlet box and are created when two, 45° bends are created on opposite sides of the conduit.

When making an offset bend, follow the steps below:

• Using the line stamped on the conduit as a guide, align the conduit in the bender. Using this line as a guide will insure a uniform offset bend **(Figure 15-B-6b)**.

• Make a 45°angle in the conduit for the first half of the bend **(Figure 15-B-6c)**.

• Next, turn the conduit over in the bender and position the conduit in the center of the first bend. Make the bend until the end of the conduit is parallel with the main piece of conduit **(Figure 15-B-6d)**.

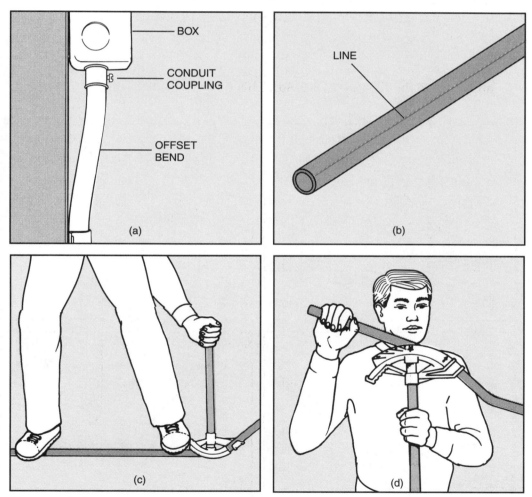

Figure 15-B-6. *Making offset bends.*

C. Installing EMT

The NEC® requires that only metal device and outlet boxes and approved metal couplings and connectors may be used when installing EMT. When installing a circuit in EMT, the EMT functions as both the equipment ground and protection for the conductors inside it. This means that the equipment grounding conductor normally required for circuits using NM cable is not necessary when using this type of installation. Only two conductors are required for 120-volt and 240-volt circuits. However, circuits requiring both 120 and 240-volts, such as ranges and dryers, will still require three conductors.

EMT may installed through holes drilled in joists, studs and rafters much like NM cable **(Figure 15-C-1)** or it can be installed to the wall's finished surface **(Figure 15-C-2).** Outlet boxes are loosely mounted to the framing until the conduit connections have been completed. This allows for minor adjustments between the box, conduit and couplings. After adjustments are made, outlet boxes can be securely fastened in place.

EMT cannot be threaded. It is commonly installed using mechanical connectors of the type shown in the illustrations below. This type is called a **set screw** connector. For a water tight connection, compression connectors may also be used. Different types of connectors are available for installing rigid conduit, armored or flexible metal conduit, liquid tight conduit, EPVC conduit and flexible nonmetallic conduit.

Connections must be made correctly to insure that the system is electrically and mechanically connected. It must be properly grounded at every point along the circuit if it is to function safely.

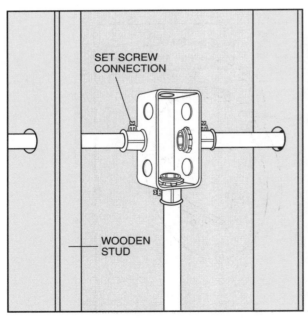

Figure 15-C-1. *EMT may be installed through holes in wood frame construction. It must be connected with approved connectors.*

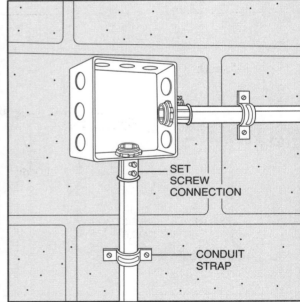

Figure 15-C-2. *EMT and other types of conduit may also be installed on the finished wall surfaces using conduit straps.*

D. Installing Conductors in EMT

After the conduit has been installed, electrical conductors can then be pulled from outlet to outlet along the circuit run. When performing this part of the task, three important considerations must be observed:

- Only two (2) hot conductors for 120- volt and 240-volt circuits are required for EMT, IMC or rigid metallic conduit installations. The conduit serves as the equipment grounding conductor. Although not required, an equipment grounding conductor may be installed in the conduit if desired. Modern equipment will perform with fewer problems when an equipment grounding conductor is installed.

- No conductor splices are permitted inside the conduit. Conductors must be solid and continuous from outlet to outlet.

- No substitutions for conductor color coding are permitted.

Author's Note: Although not required by the NEC®, good wiring practice suggests installing a grounding conductor in the conduit.

For short runs, it may be possible to simply push the conductors from one outlet to another. For longer runs, or those with several bends, you will need a tool called a **fish-tape**.

A **fish-tape** is typically used for pulling conductors through conduit **(Figure 15-D-1)**. It consists of a flexible metal tape with a loop (hook) on the end, approximately 1/8-inch wide and available in lengths of 50 to 100 feet long. The tape is inserted into a section of the conduit at the outlet box and pushed (or pulled) to the next outlet. The conductors are then fastened to the loop on the end of the tape. The tape is pulled back through the conduit until the conductors reach the outlet box. This process is repeated until conductors have been pulled to each outlet on the circuit run.

Author's Note CAUTION! Never use a fish tape to pull conductors into conduit or wall cavities where adjacent circuits may be energized

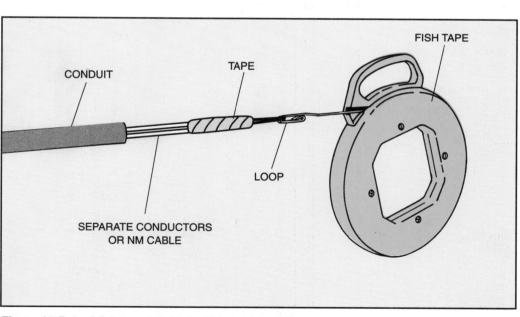

Figure 15-D-1. *A fish-tape used for pulling conductors through conduit.*

Notes

The Service Entrance

16

The service entrance is generally defined as the equipment located outside the residence that makes it possible to provide electrical power to the service entrance panel. This equipment includes the **service drop conductors** and **meter,** usually supplied and installed by the utility supplier and the **entrance head, service mast, insulators, mounting brackets, service entrance conductors** and **meter base,** customarily installed by the electrical contractor. Technically, the service drop conductors and the meter are the property of the utility supplier and do not belong to the homeowner. Once all equipment has been installed, inspected and approved, the utility company will connect the service drop to the service entrance conductors, completing the installation.

Two methods by which the power is delivered to the residence are the **overhead service drop** and the **underground service lateral**. The most common installation is the overhead service drop **(Figure 16-1)**. This method delivers power from power lines located above ground to the service entrance equipment at the residence. Service lateral installations deliver power in lines located underground.

A. Service Drops

B. Types of Service Drops

C. Installing Service Entrance Equipment

D. Meter Base Connections

E. Service Laterals

Figure 16-1. *An overhead service drop typical of the type used for residential service entrance installations.*

A. Service Drops

The **service drop** can be defined as the service conductors that supply power from the utility supplier to the attachment point at the residential structure. **(Figure 16-A-1)**. It is usually located and installed by the power supplier. The point of attachment of the service drop to the residence is usually dependant upon the relative location of the distribution power lines and the location of the meter and service entrance panel at the residence.

NEC® Reference
For more on
service drop
requirements,
see NEC® Article
230-26

Selecting the location for the service entrance equipment and the service drop should always be decided upon by mutual agreement between the electrical contractor and the power supplier. It is usually the responsibility of the power supplier to deliver the service drop or service lateral to the point of connection at the dwelling. It is a good practice to always contact the power supplier to make sure who is responsible for each phase of the service entrance installation.

Service drop conductors are connected to a building at the **service entrance head** (also called **weather head**). The entrance head serves as the connection point for the service drop conductors and the service entrance connectors at the residence. It also helps protect the service entrance conductors as they enter the residence. The point of attachment may be an insulator on the service mast or an eyebolt attached to a supporting member of the dwelling **(Figure 16-A-2)**. These provide the connection and support points for the neutral conductor which also supports the weight of the service drop.

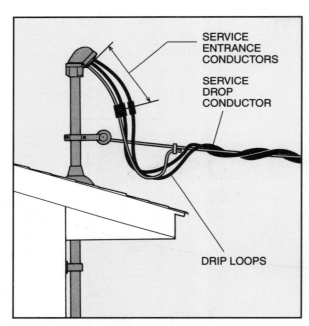

Figure 16-A-1. *Service drop conductors are connected to the service entrance conductors at the service entrance head.*

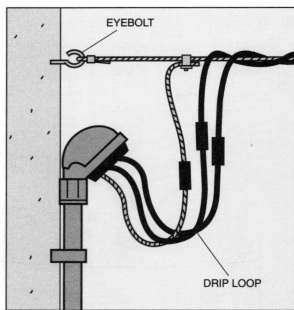

Figure 16-A-2. *Service drop conductors may be supported by an eyebolt or and insulator installed to the surface of the building.*

■ Service Drop Installation Requirements

Service drop installations used in new construction are required to have two insulated conductors and a bare neutral conductor. Most installations use **triplex cable (Figure 16-A-3, inset)**. The insulated conductors wrap around and are supported by the neutral conductor which is used to anchor the cable to the mast or to the eyebolt or insulator installed on the building surface.

The NEC® requires that service drop conductors whose rating is not in excess of 600 volts, be installed with minimum clearances above final ground grade. **Figure 16-A-3** below illustrates some of the minimum clearance requirements for service drops allowed by the NEC®. Some power suppliers and local codes may have requirements that differ from those in the NEC®. Check with both the power supplier and your local building codes when planning the service drop installation.

- **10 Feet** - the minimum clearance required at the service entrance to buildings or at the drip loop of the building's service entrance above sidewalk level accessible to pedestrian traffic only. The voltage rating for service conductors at this height is limited to 150 volts.

- **12 Feet** - the minimum clearance required for service drops above residential property, driveways and commercial areas not subject to truck traffic. Voltage ratings for service conductors at this height is limited to 300 volts.

- **15 Feet** - the clearance requirements for service conductors at this height are the same as those for 12 ft. except the service conductor ratings may exceed 300 volts.

- **18 Feet** - minimum clearance required above pubic streets, alleys, roads, parking areas subject to truck traffic, driveways other than residential property and agricultural areas.

*NEC® Reference
For more on service drop minimum clearance requirements, see NEC® Article 230-24*

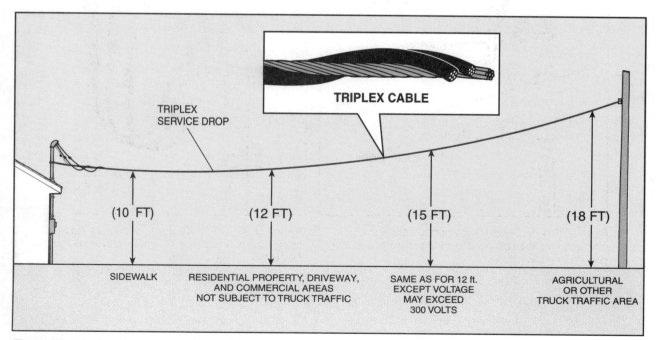

TRIPLEX CABLE

TRIPLEX SERVICE DROP

(10 FT)   (12 FT)   (15 FT)   (18 FT)

SIDEWALK | RESIDENTIAL PROPERTY, DRIVEWAY, AND COMMERCIAL AREAS NOT SUBJECT TO TRUCK TRAFFIC | SAME AS FOR 12 ft. EXCEPT VOLTAGE MAY EXCEED 300 VOLTS | AGRICULTURAL OR OTHER TRUCK TRAFFIC AREA

Figure 16-A-3. Service drop height requirements.

■ **Minimum Clearance Requirements**

The vertical clearances for all service drop conductors are based on a conductor temperature of 60° F (15°C), no wind, with final unloaded sag in the cable. Consult the NEC® for a complete description of the minimum clearances and any exceptions that may exist. Some typical minimum clearances for service drop conductors are:

*NEC® References
For more on service
drop minimum
clearances, see
NEC® Articles
230-9*

- **18 inches** - minimum clearance above the roof if the service drop is terminated at the service mast **(Figure 16-A-4)** and does not cross more than 6 feet over the overhang portion of the roof .

- **3 feet** - minimum clearance if the roof pitch is not less than 4 in 12 inches and the voltage rating does not exceed 300 volts.

- **8 feet** - minimum clearance if the service drop passes directly over the roof of another building.**)**

- **3 feet** - minimum clearance near windows, doors, porches, fire escapes or similar locations for open conductors only **(Figure 16-A-5)**. Conductors having overall outer jackets do not require a 3 ft. clearance.

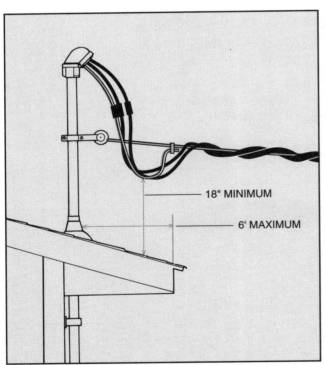

Figure 16-A-4. *Service entrance conductors terminated at the service mast must be at least 18 inches above the roof.*

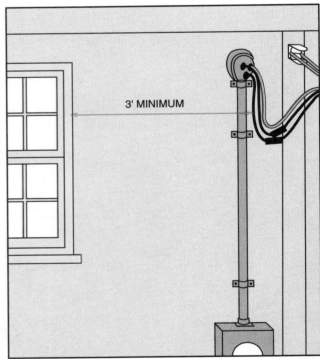

Figure 16-A-5. *Open service entrance conductors at the weatherhead installed near a window requires a 3 ft. minimum clearance.*

B. Types of Service Drops

Service entrance drops are typically connected to a building by one of three basic methods. Each of these methods is approved by the NEC®, but you should check your local electrical code and your utility supplier to determine which type is permitted for use in your area.

■ Service Mast Through-the- Roof

On most single-story structures with lower roof lines, a service mast made from conduit is a preferred method for installing the service entrance **(Figure 16-B-1).** A service mast provides both the ability to achieve the proper height requirements and protection for the service entrance conductors. It must also be of sufficient strength to support the weight of the service drop. The mast is usually made of 2 inch to 2-1/2 -inch diameter rigid conduit which extends from the meter, through the roof, to the required height above the roof line.

Service mast kits which include conduit, mounting brackets, roof flashing, entrance head and other materials necessary for a complete installation are available.

Figure 16-B-1. *Example of a through-the-roof service mast.*

■ Service Mast Attached to Building Surface

Service entrance masts may also be installed to the building surface below the roof line **(Figure 16-B-2)** provided they meet the service drop height requirements. In addition to rigid conduit, EPVC, IMC and EMT conduit may also be permitted for this installation. Again, the installation must meet NEC® and local code height and installation requirements

■ Cable Attached to Building Surface

This method was once the primary method for installing the service entrance to the structure. However, because safety and vertical clearance height requirements have increased the popularity of service mast and service lateral installations, its use has diminished.

The entrance head and the SE cable are attached to the surface of the structure using approved cable straps and/or clamps **(Figure 16-B-3)**. The weight of the service drop is supported by an eyebolt attached directly to a part of the structure that will sufficiently support the weight of the service drop. The uninsulated neutral conductor in the triplex cable is connected to the eyebolt as the point of attachment and support for the service drop conductors.

Figure 16-B-2. *Example of a service mast attached to the building's surface.*

Figure 16-B-3. *Example the weather head and service entrance cable attached to the building's surface.*

C. Installing Service Entrance Equipment

Whether installing an overhead service drop or an underground service lateral, the service entrance location, how it will be installed and what materials will be needed are all factors that must be determined before installation can begin. It is the responsibility of the electrical installer, in cooperation with the utility supplier, to locate and mount the meter base and make the connections after the service drop has been installed. Once all connections have been completed, the power supplier will mount the meter in the meter base cabinet.

■ Locating the Meter Base

The meter base is typically installed at a recommended height 4 to 5 feet above ground level at a point where the service entrance conductors will enter the structure **(Figure 16-C-1)**. It is surface mounted to the outer wall of the building with screws inserted through mounting holes in the back panel of the cabinet. Where the meter is located and how it is mounted provides a point of reference from which all other installation measurements can be made. Once the meter location has been determined, a hole must be made in the wall to route the conductors from the meter to the SEP. The hole is usually located directly beneath a knockout at the meter cabinet or behind a knockout on the back panel of the cabinet **(Figure 16-C-2)**.

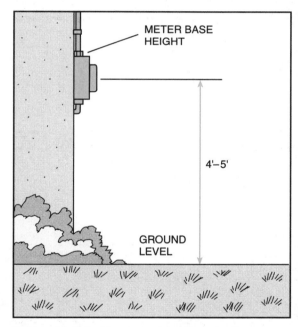

Figure 16-C-1. *The meter base is typically installed to the surface of the exterior wall 4 to 5 ft. above ground level.*

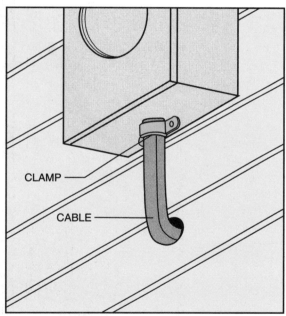

Figure 16-C-2. *The service entrance conductors can be routed from the meter base through holes in the exterior wall located below or directly through the back wall of the meter base cabinet.*

■ Service Entrance Materials & Equipment

The basic materials and equipment necessary for installing an overhead service entrance mast include conductors, entrance head, conduit and approved conduit connectors and a meter base. Kits containing these materials are available at most electrical supply houses.

- **Conductors** - Because conduit provides protection against weather and/or mechanical damage, separate conductors are typically used for installation; a cable with an outer covering is not required **(Figure 16-C-3a)**. However, SE cable may is also commonly used for service entrance installation.

- **Entrance heads** - Entrance heads are designed for use with conduit and for SE cable only installations. Entrance heads used with conduit may be joined to the conduit by threads **(Figure 16-C-3b)** or bolt-on clamps. Entrance heads installed without the use of conduit must be of the bolt-on type **(Figure 16-C-3c)**. Make sure you ask for the proper type when buying service entrance equipment and materials.

- **Conduit and conduit connectors -** Conduit may be rigid metal, IMT, EMT or EPVC **(Figure 16-C-3d)**. The inside surface of conduit has a smooth surface which makes it ideal for pulling electrical conductors through it. You must determine which type is required for the job by checking with your local building inspector and/or the NEC®. All conduit must carry the UL label and meet NEC® and local code requirements.

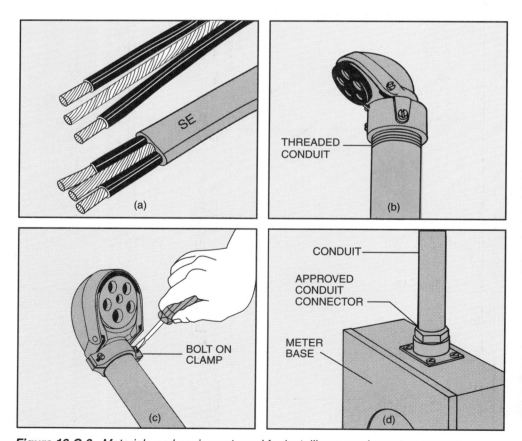

Figure 16-C-3. *Materials and equipment used for installing a service entrance mast.*

Installing A Service Mast Through The Roof

Follow the procedures below for installing a service mast through the roof **(Figure 16-C-4)**:

- Carefully measure and cut the length of conduit needed.

- Locate and cut the a hole in the roof aligned with the meter base below.

- Insert the conduit through the hole cut in the roof and raise the mast into position above the roof. Fasten the mast in place with the appropriate support brackets. Install the roof flashing cap and seal with roof cement if necessary.

- Install the necessary bolts, brackets, guy wires and other mast supports.

- Install the insulator bracket and insulator at the required height above the roof surface.

- Install the service mast to the meter base using the proper water proof connectors.

- Make any necessary alignment adjustments between the mast and the meter base before securely attaching the mast to the structure.

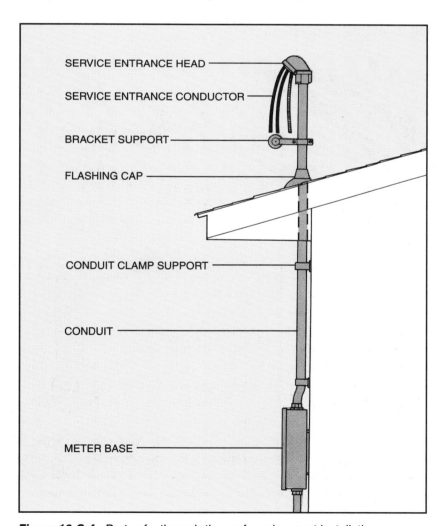

Figure 16-C-4. *Parts of a through-the-roof service mast installation.*

■ Installing Service Entrance Conductors in Conduit

Conductors used for service entrance installations in conduit may be individual conductors or you may also use SE cable. Consult the tables in the NEC® **for a** complete listing of the types allowable. The neutral conductor in the service entrance cable is not required to be insulated. However, if insulated, it must be white or grey in color. Insulated conductors may be black, red or one black and one red. To install the conductors in conduit between the entrance head and the meter base:

- Carefully measure the length of cable/conductors you will need for the installation and cut to the proper length. Allow an extra 3 ft. of conductor length for making connections at the entrance head and an extra 8 to 10 inches conductor length inside the meter base for making meter terminal connections **(Figure 16-C-5)**.

- With the entrance head removed from the top of the conduit, push the SE cable/conductors down through the mast conduit until it enters the meter base cabinet.

- Insert the conductors through the holes in the entrance head and replace the entrance head securely to the top of the service mast **(Figure 16-C-6)**.

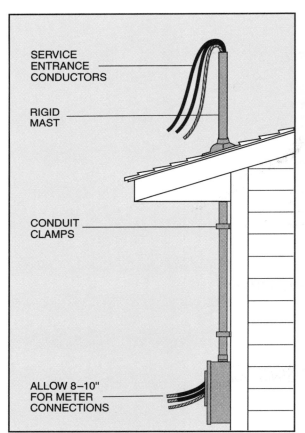

Figure 16-C-5. *Allow approximately 3 ft. of conductor length at the top of the mast for inserting in to the entrance head a making service drop connections. Allow 8-10 inches of conductor length in the meter base for meter terminal connections.*

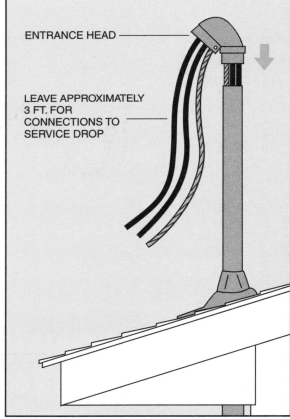

Figure 16-C-6. *Insert the service entrance conductors in the mast head and attach the assembly to the top of the service mast.*

◼ Installing a Service Entrance Using SE Cable

To install a service entrance using SE cable only follow these suggested procedures **(Figure 16-C-7)**:

- Measure and cut the service cable to the length required. Remove approximately 3 ft. of the outer jacket of the cable exposing the separate conductors.

- Insert the conductors in the bushing holes in the entrance head. Remember to leave approximately 3 ft. extra length for the service drop connections. Connect the entrance head to the service entrance cable with and approved clamp.

- Mount the assembled service entrance head and cable into position on the surface of the building directly above and vertically aligned at the point it enters the meter base.

- Pull at least 8 to 10 inches of cable inside the meter base for making meter based terminal connections. Secure the cable to the meter base using an appropriate weather-proof connector.

- Secure the service cable to the side of the building with support straps or clamps at 30-inch intervals. The cable must be secured to the structure within 12 inches of the meter base cabinet.

Author's Note: Make sure there is enough cable to reach the service drop support point and for making drop loop connections.

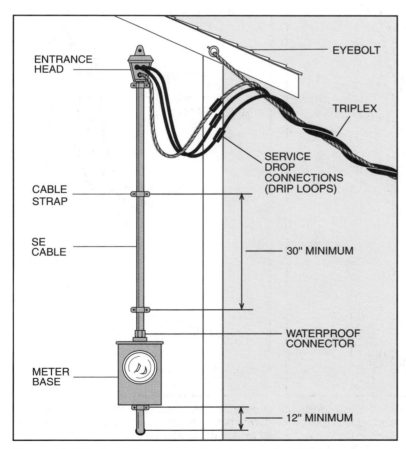

Figure 16-C-7. A service entrance installation using SE cable attached to the surface of the building.

D. Meter Base Connections

To complete the service equipment installation, service entrance conductors must be installed from the meter base to the service entrance panel. Two methods of installation are typically used.

■ Routing SE Cable Through the Wall

Routing SE cable/conductors from the meter base to the SEP directly through the wall is typical for most residential meter to SEP installations. **Figure 16-D-1** illustrates this type of installation:

- Make a hole through the wall of the structure just below the knockout at the bottom of the meter base cabinet.

- Pull the cable through the knockout into the meter base and secure it to the meter base cabinet with an approved clamp or connector.

- Route the cable from the meter base to the SEP cabinet making gradual bends in the cable along the route. Attach the cable to the framework at the recommended intervals. Seal the hole around the cable with a weather proof caulking or sealant.

- Insert the cable through a knockout in the SEP cabinet and secure with a clamp. It may enter at either the top of the cabinet or the bottom of the cabinet. Pull enough cable inside the SEP cabinet to adequately make connections at the main breaker terminal.

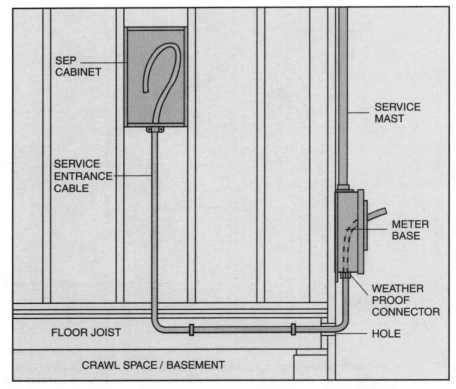

Figure 16-D-1. *Installing service entrance cable from the meter base through the wall to the service entrance panel.*

Routing SE Conductors in Conduit

Routing SE conductors in conduit is an option which may be permitted by some local codes but required in others **(Figure 16-D-2)**. Be sure to check with your local building inspection office. Below are some simple steps for making this type of installation.

- Install the conduit between the SEP and the meter base. The conduit extends through a knockout at the back of the meter cabinet and is secured with an approved weatherproof connector or bushing.

- Route the conduit through a hole made in the wall of the residence.

- Connect the conduit to the SEP cabinet with an approved connector.

  NOTE: When using metallic conduit, a grounding bushing is required at the connection point where the conduit joins the SEP cabinet. The bushing is bonded to the neutral bus bar in the SEP by a jumper conductor (Figure 16-D-2 inset).

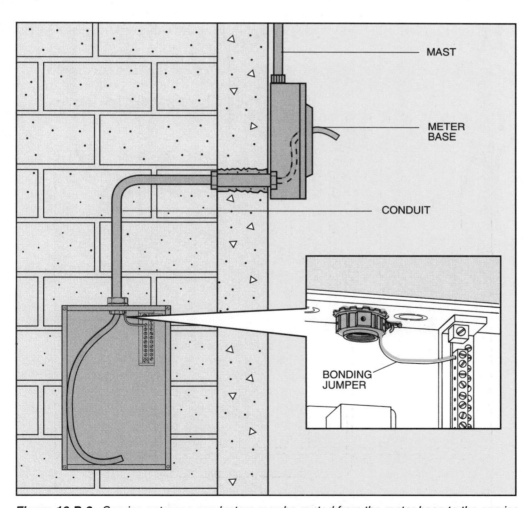

Figure 16-D-2. *Service entrance conductors may be routed from the meter base to the service entrance panel through conduit. (Inset) Metal conduit must be bonded to the grounding bus with a grounding bushing and bonding jumper.*

■ Making Meter Base Terminal Connections

After all equipment for the service entrance have been installed meter base connections can be made. These connections will join the conductors from the entrance head to the meter **(line side)** and the conductors from the meter base to the service entrance panel **(load side).**

Figure 16-D-3 below illustrates a typical meter base connections for three-wire overhead service. **Figure 16-D-4** illustrates typical meter base connections for three-wire underground service (lateral service). The same meter base may be used for either type of installation.

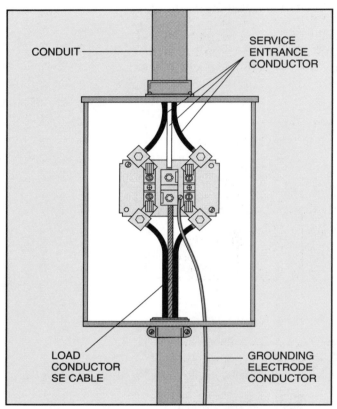

Figure 16-D-3. *Meter connections for a typical three-wire overhead service installation.*

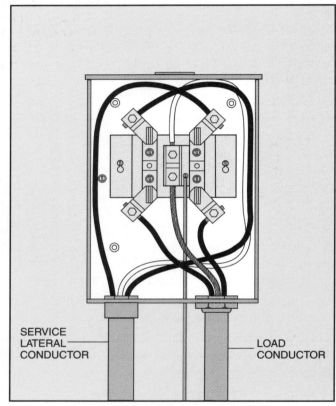

Figure 16-D-4. *Meter connections for a typical three-wire underground service lateral.*

E. Service Laterals

Underground electrical service installation continues to gain favor as a means of electrical power delivery. Many of today's residential buildings, as well as an increasing number of commercial developments, now select underground service. In many parts of the country, the entire distribution system is delivered by this method. In addition to the aesthetics it offers by having no overhead exposed wiring, it helps reduce damage that may be caused by lightning, wind, ice or snow and falling tree hazards. It also eliminates the danger from tall, moving equipment coming in contact with overhead wiring.

Power from the utility supplier may be delivered to the meter base at the residence in a trench from either a pole mounted transformer **(Figure 16-E-1a),** or by a pad mounted transformer located at ground level **(Figure 16-E-1b)**. Most local codes require underground service entrance cable be buried from 24 to 48 inches deep, depending on the installation location and surrounding conditions. Transformers located at ground level may be mounted on concrete pads within metal or fiberglass cabinets.

NEC® References
For more on
service lateral
installations, see,
NEC® Articles
230-9
230-24
Table 330-5

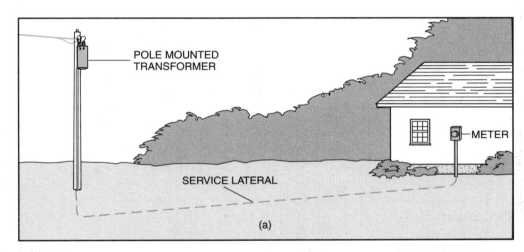

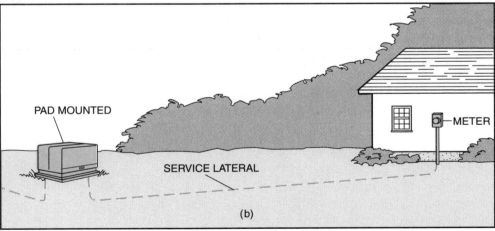

Figure 16-E-1. *Typical service lateral installations. (a) Service lateral from a pole mounted transformer. (b) Service lateral from a pad mounted transformer.*

Cable/conductors required for service lateral installations may be made of copper or aluminum and must be listed as a **USE (Underground Service Entrance)**. The conductors are protected by a tough, moisture resistant outer covering. The NEC® does not require that conductors be installed in conduit. They are commonly buried in direct contact with the earth or may be installed in conduit if there is a potential danger of the cable being damaged.

Local codes and/or utility suppliers may require special types of installation connections and fittings and equipment when supplying lateral service to a structure. Check your local codes and with your utility suppliers.

Figures 16-E-2 and **16-E-3** illustrate two approved methods for making service entrance connections to underground service laterals.

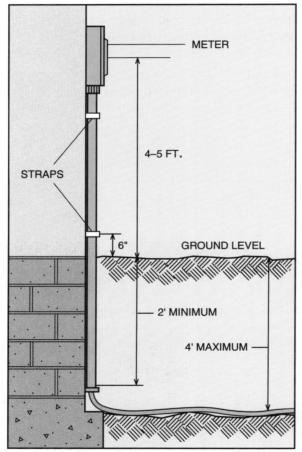

Figure 16-E-2. *Service lateral conductors must be installed a minimum of two feet below the ground surface level.*

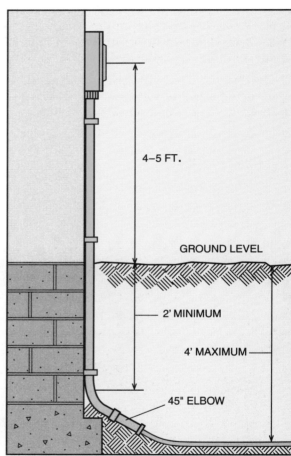

Figure 16-E-3. *Some local codes may require an elbow to bring the conductors into the conduit below grade*

Installing Lighting Fixtures 17

Installation of the lighting fixtures will be one of the last tasks you will likely perform in completing the residential wiring system. This step usually comes after all finish work— painting, wall paper and decorative trim work— has been completed.

The installation of most types of lighting fixtures, whether small and simple or large and elaborate, will require similar installations. Most fixtures can be easily installed simply by following the manufacturer's directions. Many of today's lighting fixtures come equipped with either factory installed wiring conductors **(Figure 17-1)** or conductor terminal screws **(Figure 17-2)**. All lighting fixtures must carry the UL label and meet NEC® installation requirements.

In this chapter, you will learn the basic methods for installing some types of lighting fixtures used in most new residential construction. How each type of fixture is installed is discussed as follows:

A. Direct to Outlet Box

B. Strap-to-Outlet Box

C. Installing Heavy Fixtures

D. Installing Recessed Fixtures

Figure 17-1. *A lighting fixture equipped with factory installed wiring conductors.*

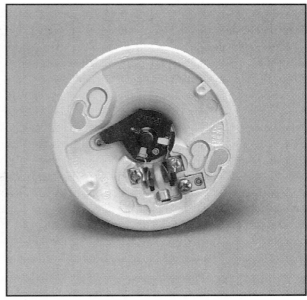

Figure 17-2. *A porcelain lighting fixture equipped with conductor terminal screws.*

A. Direct to Outlet Box

Fixtures mounted directly to the outlet box may be equipped with conductor or terminal screws such as the simple, porcelain fixture shown in **(Figure 17-A-1)**. This type of fixture is often installed in crawl spaces, storage areas and attics. They are not permitted for use in clothes closets. The connections for this type of installation require only two terminals and a grounding connection. To install a fixture directly to an outlet box, follow the steps illustrated below:

NEC® References
For more on
lighting fixture
installations, see
NEC® Articles
410-5
410-8 (b, d)

❶ Conductor Connections

- Connect the **black** conductor in the power source cable to the brass terminal screw on the fixture.

- Connect the **white** conductor to the silver terminal screw on the fixture.

- If using a metallic box, connect the grounding conductor to the **green** grounding screw in the box.

❷ Attaching the Fixture

- Fold the conductors carefully into the box

- Insert the screws (usually equipped with the fixture) through the holes in the fixture and then into the mounting tabs on the box and tighten. Fixtures of the type illustrated may be made of porcelain or heavy plastic. If the fixture is made of porcelain, make sure you do not overtighten the mounting bolts — it could break the porcelain.

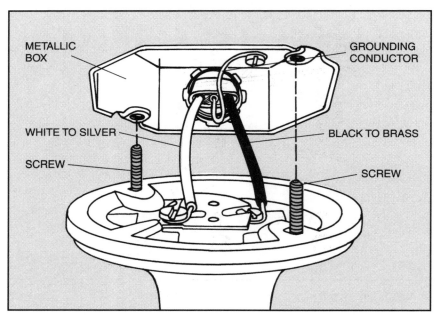

Figure 17-A-1. *A fixture mounted directly to the outlet box.*

B. Strap-To-Outlet Box

Mounting a lighting fixture to an outlet box using the strap-to-box method is one of the more common methods used for installing lighting fixtures to walls or ceilings. This style fixture mount uses a metal strap which is attached to the outlet box. The fixture is then attached to the strap using headless bolts and decorative nuts. **Figure 17-B-1** illustrates how this type of fixture is mounted to a wall outlet.

① Conductor Connections

- Connect the **black** conductors in both cables to the **black** fixture conductor.

- Connect the **white** conductors to the **white** fixture conductor.

- If using a nonmetallic box, connect the grounding conductors with a wire nut and fold them into the box. **Do not remove**

② Attaching the Fixture

- Using the small screws provided with the fixture, secure the strap to the box.

- Secure the fixture to the strap using the headless bolts. Attach the fixture cover using the decorative nuts.

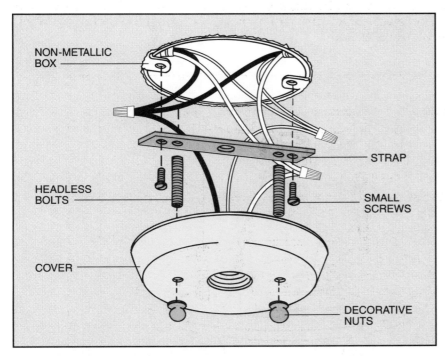

Figure 17-B-1. *A fixture mounted using a strap-to- box installation.*

C. Installing Heavy Fixtures

Large, heavy fixtures, such as large chandeliers and ceiling fans, require extra mounting support than do the smaller fixtures.Special mounting boxes and installation is required for these heavier fixtures. Two methods for mounting heavy fixtures are fixture-to-stud and ceiling fan hanger assemblies.

■ Fixture-to -Stud

NEC® References
For more on large
and heavy fixture
installations, see
NEC® Articles
370-27(a-b)
410-16
422-18 (a-b)

Fixture-to- stud mounting is often used for hanging heavy lighting fixtures that are suspended by a decorative chain or rod. It utilizes a **stud and strap** arrangement similar to that of the strap-to-box method. The fixture is secured by a decorative holding screw or nut located in the center of the fixture canopy **(Figure 17-C-1)**. To install a heavy ceiling fixture using the fixture to stud method:

- Attach the strap to the outlet box.

- Screw the stud into the strap. Make sure that enough of the stud is screwed into the strap to insure a secure connection that will not become loose over time.

- Insert the fixture conductors through the stud and connect them to the power cable.

- Slide the canopy of the fixture over the outlet box. exposing the end of the stud. Screw the fixture holding nut securely to the stud.

Author's Note:
Make sure all fixture
components are
assembled in the
proper order before
final connections are
made in the outlet
box.

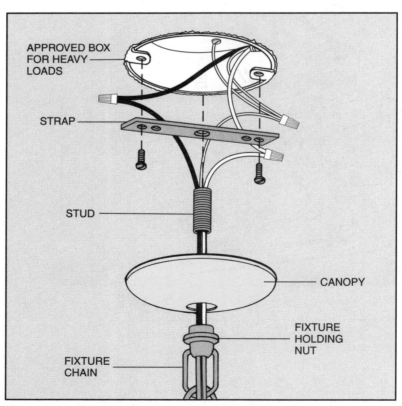

Figure 17-C-1. *A heavy fixture mounted using a stud-to-fixture installation.*

D. Installing Recessed Fixtures

Recessed fixtures, such as the one shown in **Figure 17-D-1**, are self - contained and usually do not require an outlet box in which to make the wiring connections.

Recessed fixtures are usually mounted during the rough-in stage of construction before dry wall or other wall coverings have been installed. Most are pre-wired and can be quickly installed between ceiling joists using adjustable brackets that come as part of the fixture assembly package. Wiring connections are made within the junction box on the fixture.

Fixtures may be purchased with an **insulation contact rating (IC)**. A fixture with this rating is used where insulation is allowed in direct contact with the fixture. However, many types of recessed fixtures do not carry the IC rating and do not permit direct insulation contact. Recessed fixtures that do not carry the IC rating require that no insulation can be installed within 3 inches of a recessed fixture enclosure, wiring compartment (junction box) or ballast. Unrestricted air circulation must be allowed around this type of fixture. If overheating occurs, the fixture will not function properly.

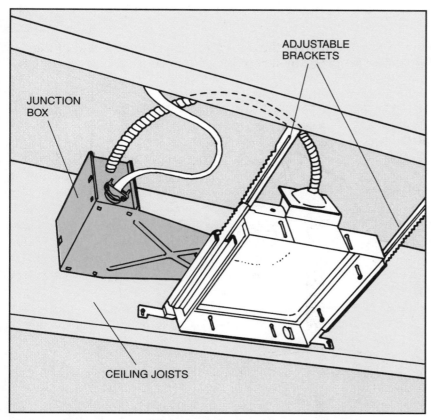

Figure 17-D-1. *Recessed fixtures are pre-wired and are mounted to the framework with screws or nails.*

Notes

Estimating Wiring Costs 18

As you gain experience in the residential wiring process, you will likely be required to estimate the costs for a wiring installation **(Figure 18-1)**. Cost estimation is an important responsibility for both large and small electrical contractors. It can also be an important factors for the homeowner who may want to do his/her own wiring installation. Each must be able to make the correct considerations for estimating both materials and labor costs. Depending on the type of wiring installation required—large or small, simple or complex— you will need some method for determining what the estimated costs are likely to be. Your method of estimating should be a complete, systematic plan for including all costs including materials equipment, labor and overhead. You may want to develop your own cost estimating form to help you in identifying the many different factors that must be included in a cost estimate. Two recognized methods of developing a wiring cost estimate are:

A. Make a Detailed Analysis

B. Make a Quick Estimate

Figure 18-1. *Learning how to estimate the costs of a wiring job is an important part of the job.*

A. Make a Detailed Analysis

The most accurate method of estimating a wiring job is by listing every detail of the wiring installation shown on the residential electrical plan. This would include a measurement for electrical cable, conduit, the number and type of electrical boxes, switches, receptacles and other devices and equipment. Special items such as service entrance panel boards and subpanels, breakers and other service entrance equipment and materials must also be included. The detailed cost for each item and the cost of installation must be totaled to arrive at a total cost estimate.

The specifications for an electrical wiring estimate should always include the following:

- The installation must comply with the NEC®, state and local codes.

- Use only UL listed materials

- Obtain homeowner approval for all fixture types and prices

- Provide a one year warranty on all work and materials.

Once all materials and labor costs have been computed, the electrical contractor must add overhead costs and a profit margin to complete the estimate. **Overhead** and **profit margins** may differ greatly depending on the area of the country, labor and material costs. Even the housing market strength in a given area of the country is a factor for determining costs. Depending on any combination of these factors, overhead and profit margins may range from a high of **50%** in a fast growth housing market to as low as **25%** to **35%** in a slow growth area.

B. Make a Quick Estimate

Two methods of making a quick estimate of wiring costs are:

(1) Averaging Outlet Costs and

(2) Estimating Separate Costs.

■ Outlet Cost Averaging Method

One of the most common methods for making a quick estimate is by averaging the cost for the total number of outlets in the residence. This total would include all receptacle outlets, lighting outlets and switch outlets. A simple example of outlet cost averaging is shown below.

Example:

Based on past knowledge and experience, an electrical contractor might estimate an average cost per outlet based on the cost in his area. This cost estimate is derived by adding together the estimated costs for all materials, equipment, and installation of all outlets on the wiring plan. The estimated overhead and profit for each outlet installation would also be added to the total.

Assuming a total of **75 outlets** are required for a wiring plan at a estimated cost per outlet of **$35.00 per outlet**. The quick estimate for the average outlet cost method for this particular job can be derived by multiplying the total number of outlets by the estimated cost per outlet:

75 outlets X $35.00 per outlet = $2625.00

Lighting fixture cost estimates must also be determined using a fixed dollar amount for the total fixture requirements to complete the job. This fixed dollar amount is mutually agreed upon by the contractor and the homeowner. The fixtures are usually selected by the homeowner. If the fixture costs exceed the fixture allowance, the difference is paid by the homeowner. Assuming a lighting fixture cost allowance is set at **$750.00**, a total cost figure for the complete wiring installation can be achieved by adding the outlet costs with the fixture costs:

$2625.00 + $750.00 = $3375.00

Below is a list of factors which must be considered when determining costs using the average outlet cost method:

1. Conductor length between outlets

2. Ceiling height

3. Device and circuit conductor ratings

4. Type and style of device and junction boxes (plastic, metal, fan box or other heavy fixture use, other)

5. Ceiling design and characteristics (flat, cathedral, other)

Note: The figures used in the above example are for illustrative purposes only. Actual costs may vary depending on the geographical region of the country and/or local conditions.

■ Separate Circuit Cost Method

A more detailed and accurate method of making a quick estimate is by determining the separate costs of all 120-volt, 240-volt and 120-240-volts outlets. The separate cost of the service entrance materials and equipment are then totaled and added to the total costs of the circuits. An example of this method is shown below.

NOTE: The figures used in the example below are arbitrary and are used for illustrative purposes only. Actual costs may vary depending on the geographical region of the country and/or local conditions.

Example:

1. **Estimate the cost for all 120-volt outlets:**

   <u>65</u> outlets @ $<u>20.00</u> each = $<u>1300.00</u>

2. **Estimate the costs for all 240-volt outlets:**

   <u>5</u> outlets @ $<u>100.00</u> each = $<u>500.00</u>

3. **Estimate the costs for all 120-240-volt outlets:**

   <u>4</u> outlets @ $ <u>125.00</u> each = $<u>500.00</u>

4. **Estimate the cost for the service entrance equipment (panel board, breakers, cables, etc). This may be done by applying a per ampere for the selected service entrance panel. For example, a**

   <u>200</u> ampere panel board @ $ <u>4.00</u> per ampere = $<u>800.00</u>

5. **Total for items 1 through 4 = $<u>3100.00</u>**

6. **Add 25% for overhead and profit margin: $<u>775.00</u>**

7. **Total estimate = $<u>3875.00</u>**

It is important to remember good judgment must always be applied when arriving at an accurate cost estimate. Be sure to consider items in the estimate whose cost may be more than usual or customary include these special costs in your estimate. Two examples are shown below.

Examples:

● A 240 -volt basement circuit installed parallel with the floor joists will cost less to install than a similar circuit installed through holes the floor joists. The labor and time for drilling holes in the joists is an expense that must be considered.

● A service entrance panel installation that requires long runs for each circuit will add considerable cost to the installation in materials and labor. Locating the SEP in the most convenient location as required by the NEC® or by adding a subpanel will help eliminate the expense of long circuit runs and extra labor.

Below is an example for estimating the cost of a general purpose circuit shown on a the sample wiring plan.

Using general purpose circuit #4 on the sample wiring plan as an example, **Figure 18-B-1** illustrates a simple method for estimating the cost of circuit The estimate includes all outlet and device boxes, cable, switches, receptacles and approximate labor and overhead costs. It does not include an overcurrent protection device nor cost of the subpanel.

Cost Estimate - General Purpose Circuit #4
(Bedroom #1/Bathroom #1)

(5) Single gang device boxes: @ **$.75 ea.**	$5.25
(1) Triple gang device boxes: @ **$2.75 ea.**	$2.75
(4) Lighting outlet boxes: @ **$1.00 ea.**	$4.00
(1) UL approved fan box @ **$16.00 ea.**	$16.00
(5) Single -Pole Switches (20 Amp) @ **$2.00 ea.**	$10.00
(175 Ft) 12-2 w/ground NM cable @ **$.80 per ft.**	$136.00
Labor: ____4____ Hrs @ **15.00 per hr.**	$100.00
Total: materials and labor	$275.00
Overhead: Add 25% to materials and labor	
total (after taxes and fees)	$78.75
TOTAL	$353.75

NOTE: Prices of items shown above are for illustrative purposes only. Actual prices will vary

Figure 18-B-1. *A simple method for estimating the cost of one circuit.*

Notes

Appendix A

Load Calculations (Optional Method)

NEC Article	Circuit Type	Rating	Total Calculated Load
220-3b(2)	Lighting	_____ VA **X** _____ sq. ft.	_____ VA
210-52b	Small Appliance	_____ VA **X** 2 circuits	_____ VA
220-16b	Laundry	_____ VA **X** 1 circuit	_____ VA
	Fixed Appliances	**Nameplate Ratings**	
220-3b(3)	Range	_____ KVA	_____ KVA
220-30	Oven	_____ KVA	_____ KVA
	Cook Top	_____ KVA	_____ KVA
	Garbage Disposal	_____ KVA	_____ KVA
	Dishwasher	_____ KVA	_____ KVA
	Trash Compactor	_____ KVA	_____ KVA
	Clothes Dryer	_____ KVA	_____ KVA
	Water Heater	_____ KVA	_____ KVA
	Other	_____ KVA	_____ KVA
	Total: All Circuits		_____ **KVA**
220-30	**Demand Factors:**		
	10 KVA @ 100%	_____	_____ KVA
	Remainder @ 40%	_____	_____ KVA
	Select Larger of the following (use name plate rating)		
	100% of AC or Heat Pump	_____ KVA	_____ KVA
	100% of thermal storage (or other heating systems)	_____ KVA	_____ KVA
	65% of Central Electric Furnace and Heat Pump Strip Heat (if less than 4 units)	_____ KVA	_____ KVA
	65% of Electric Space Heaters	_____ KVA	_____ KVA
	40% of Electric Space Heaters (if more than 4 units)	_____ KVA	_____ KVA
	Total KVA: All Loads		_____ **KVA**
	Minimum Service Panel _____ = Amps	**Recommended Panel Size =** _____	

Appendix B

National Joint Apprenticeship and Training Committee for the Electrial Industry (NJATC)
16201 Trade Zone Avenue, Suite 105, Upper Malboro, MD 20772
Phone: 301-249-2042   Fax: 301-249-4961
email: office@njatc.org
http://www.njatc.org

International Association of Electrical Inspectors (IAEI)
901 Waterfall Way, Suite 602, Richardson , TX 75080-7702
Phone: 972-235-1455   Fax: 972-235-3855
email: iaei@compuserve.com
http://www.iaei.com

International Brotherhood of Electrical Workers (IBEW)
Mr. Hill International Secretary-Treasurer
Washington, DC
Phone: 202-728-7000 Fax: 202-728-6123

National Electrical Contractors Association (NECA)
Atlanta NECA Chapter
576 Trabert Avenue, NW
Atlanta, Georgia 30309
Phone: 404-352-2500 Fax: 404-355-2243

National Electrical Safety Foundation (NESF)
1300 North 17th Street, Suite 1847, Rosslyn, VA 22209
Phone: 703-841-3211   Fax: 703-841-3311

Southeastern Electrification Council
4225 University Avenue, Columbus, GA 31907-5645
Phone: 706-569-3186   Fax: 706-565-3564
http://www.seec.org

Acknowledgments

AAVIM wishes to express its appreciation to the following individuals, companies and organizations for their assistance in the development of this publication.

American Iron and Steel Institute
1101 17th St.
Washington, DC 20036-4700

Adjust A Box
Veco Products, Inc.
P.O. Box 692
Lyle, WA 98635

Badcock Home Furnishings
2215 Lexington Rd.
Athens, GA

Carlon Electrical Products
A. Lamson & Session Company
25701 Science Park Drive
Cleveland, Ohio 44122

Carl Scholfield
172 E. Oglethorpe Avenue
Lyons, GA. 30436

Challenger Electrical Equipment Corporation
508 Lapp Road
Malvern, PA 19355

Cutler-Hammer
Five Parkway Center
Pittsburgh, PA 15220

Dana Perkins, Area Teacher of Agriculture Education
Four Towers
University of Georgia
Athens, GA 30602

Farm Electric, Inc.
1045 Baxter St.
Athens, GA 30604

Gene Fields, Inc.
160 Oakmont Ct.
Winterville, GA 30683

Hodges Ace Hardware
East Plaza Shopping Center
Lexington Rd.
Athens, GA 30605

Jerry Taylor
Agriculture Instructor
Madison County High School
Danielsville, Georgia

June Walker
1623 Meriweather Dr.
Bogart, GA 30622

Ken Hix, Chief Electrical Code Analyst
Athens-Clarke County Building and Permits Department
120 W. Dougherty St.
Athens, GA 30603

Lowe's of Athens
Epps Bridge Road
Athens, GA 30604

National Food and Energy Council
409 Vandiver West Suite 202
Columbia, MO. 65202

The Home Depot
Epps Bridge Rd.
Athens GA 30604

Southwire Company
One Southwire Drive
Carrollton, Georgia 30119

Square D Company
Highway 64 East
Knightdale, NC 27545

Tay Mac Corporation
2440 West 12th St.
Suite 5
Tempe, AZ 85281

Williams True Value Hardware
3270 Lexington Rd.
Athens, GA 30605

Index